THE PLAY
CHORD SONGB(

CW00346851

Published by
Wise Publications
14-15 Berners Street, London, W1T 3LJ, UK.

Exclusive distributors:
Music Sales Limited,
Distribution Centre, Newmarket Road,
Bury St Edmunds, Suffolk, IP33 3YB, UK.
Music Sales Pty Limited
120 Rothschild Avenue, Rosebery,
NSW 2018, Australia.

Order No. AM992057
ISBN 978-1-84772-307-9

This publication is not authorised for sale in the United States of America and / or Canada

This book © Copyright 2007 Wise Publications,
a division of Music Sales Limited.

Unauthorised reproduction of any part of this
publication by any means including photocopying
is an infringement of copyright.

Compiled by Nick Crispin.
Arranged by Matt Cowe.
Music processed by Paul Ewers Music Design.
Edited by Sam Harrop.

Printed in the EU.

WISE PUBLICATIONS
part of The Music Sales Group

London / New York / Paris / Sydney / Copenhagen / Berlin / Madrid / Tokyo

www.musicsales.com

An End Has A Start

Words & Music by
Tom Smith, Russell Leetch, Chris Urbanowicz & Ed Lay

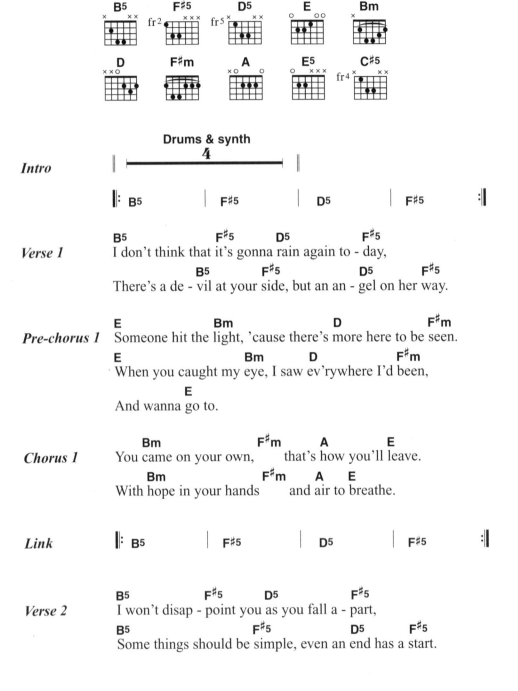

Intro

Drums & synth
$\frac{4}{4}$

‖: B5 | F♯5 | D5 | F♯5 :‖

Verse 1

B5   F♯5   D5   F♯5
I don't think that it's gonna rain again to - day,
                  B5   F♯5   D5   F♯5
There's a de - vil at your side, but an an - gel on her way.

Pre-chorus 1

E   Bm   D   F♯m
Someone hit the light, 'cause there's more here to be seen.
E   Bm   D   F♯m
When you caught my eye, I saw ev'rywhere I'd been,
                E
And wanna go to.

Chorus 1

      Bm   F♯m   A   E
You came on your own,   that's how you'll leave.
      Bm   F♯m   A E
With hope in your hands   and air to breathe.

Link

‖: B5 | F♯5 | D5 | F♯5 :‖

Verse 2

B5   F♯5   D5   F♯5
I won't disap - point you as you fall a - part,
B5   F♯5   D5   F♯5
Some things should be simple, even an end has a start.

© Copyright 2007 Soul Kitchen Music Limited.
Kobalt Music Publishing Limited.
All Rights Reserved. International Copyright Secured.

Pre-chorus 2   As Pre-chorus 1

Chorus 2

      Bm   F♯m   A   E
You came on your own,   that's how you'll leave.
      Bm   F♯m   A   E
With hope in your hands   and air to breathe.
         Bm   F♯m A   E
You'll lose ev'rything,   by the end.
       Bm   F♯m   A   E
Still my broken wings,   you find time to mend.

Bridge

    D5   F♯5   E5 C♯5 D5   F♯5   E5
More and more peo - ple I   know are getting ill.
    D5   F♯5   E5 C♯5 D5 F♯5   E5
Pull some - thing good from the   ashes now be still.

Chorus 3

      Bm   F♯m   A   E
You came on your own,   that's how you'll leave.
      Bm   F♯m   A   E
With hope in your hands   and air to breathe.
         Bm   F♯m A   E
You'll lose ev'rything,   by the end.
       Bm   F♯m   A   E
Still my broken wings,   you choose to mend.
      Bm   F♯m   A   E
You came on your own,   that's how you'll leave.
      Bm   F♯m   A   E
You came on your own,   that's how you'll leave.

Outro

B5	F♯5	D5	F♯5	
B5	F♯5	D5	F♯5	
B5 (on your own.)	F♯5	D5	F♯5	(You came
B5 (on your own.)	F♯5	D5	F♯5	(You came

3

All My Friends

Words & Music by
James Murphy

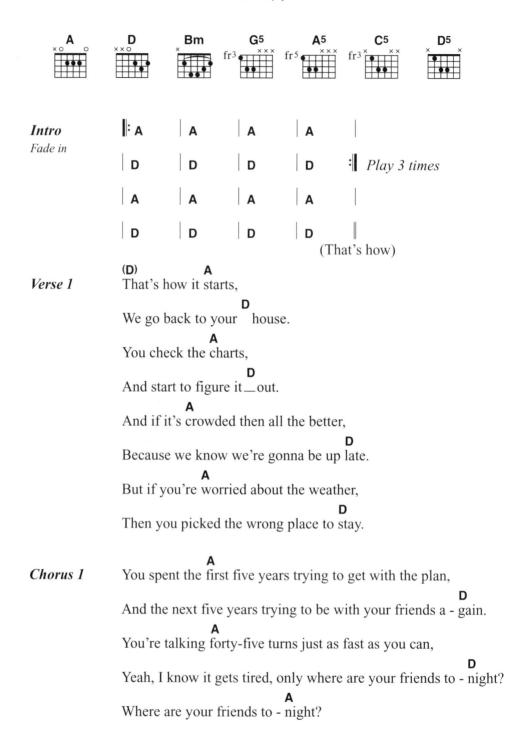

Intro
Fade in

‖: A | A | A | A |

| D | D | D | D :‖ *Play 3 times*

| A | A | A | A |

| D | D | D | D ‖

(That's how)

Verse 1

   (D)   A
That's how it starts,

                D
We go back to your house.

           A
You check the charts,

               D
And start to figure it＿out.

        A
And if it's crowded then all the better,

                    D
Because we know we're gonna be up late.

        A
But if you're worried about the weather,

                  D
Then you picked the wrong place to stay.

Chorus 1

             A
You spent the first five years trying to get with the plan,

                                                    D
And the next five years trying to be with your friends a - gain.

             A
You're talking forty-five turns just as fast as you can,

                                              D
Yeah, I know it gets tired, only where are your friends to - night?

             A
Where are your friends to - night?

© Copyright 2007 Guy With Head And Arms Music, USA.
Kobalt Music Publishing Limited.
All Rights Reserved. International Copyright Secured.

Verse 2
(A)
And so it starts,

                   D
You switch the engine on.

         A
We set controls for the heart of the sun,

                 D
One of the ways we show our age.

         A
And if the sun comes up, if the sun comes up,

                               D
And if the sun comes up and I still don't wanna stagger home.

         A
Then it's the memory of our betters

               D
That's keeping us on our feet.

           A
Chorus 2   You spent the first five years trying to get with the plan,

                            D
And the next five years trying to be with your friends a - gain.

         A
You're talking forty-five turns just as fast as you can,

                             D
Yeah, I know it gets tired, only where are your friends to - night?

             A
Where are your friends to - night?

             D
Where are your friends to - night?

             A
Where are your friends to - night?

             D
Where are your friends to - night?

             Bm
Where are your friends to - night?

             D
Where are your friends to - night?

             (A)
Where are your friends to - night?

Link 1 | **A** | **A** | **A** | **A** |
    (night.)
    | **D** | **D** | **D** | **D**   ‖
                              (It comes)

Verse 3

(D)   A
It comes a - part,

                D
The way it does in bad films,

         A
Except the part

            D
Where the moral kicks in.

         A
Although we're running out of the drugs,

                  D
And the conversation's grinding a - way.

     A
Oh, I wouldn't trade one stupid decision

           D
For another five years of life.

Chorus 3

(D)   A
You spend the first five years trying to get with the plan,

                          D
And the next five years trying to be with your friends a - gain.

         A
You're talking forty-five turns just as fast as you can,

                       D
Yeah, I know it gets tired, only where are your friends to - night?

         A
Where are your friends to - night?

          D
Where are your friends to - night?

         G5   A5   G5 A5 C5 D5 C5 D5
Where are your friends to - night?

Outro

G5 A5   G5   A5   C5   D5
    If I could be with my friends to - night.

        C5   D5   G5
If I could be with my friends to - night.

A5   G5   A5   C5   D5
If I could be with my friends to - night.

        C5   D5   G5
If I could be with my friends to - night.

A5   G5   A5   C5   D5
If I could be with my friends to - night.

        C5   D5   G5
If I could be with my friends to - night.

A5   G5   A5   C5   D5
If I could be with my friends to - night.

        C5   D5   A
If I could be with my friends to - night.

The Angry Mob

Words & Music by
Charlie Wilson, Nicholas Hodgson, Andrew White, James Rix & Nicholas Baines

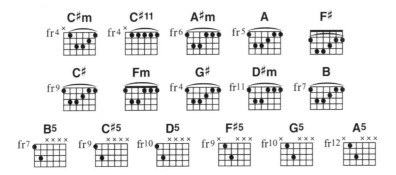

Intro

‖: C♯m C♯11 C♯m C♯11 | C♯m C♯11 C♯m C♯11 :‖

‖: C♯m C♯11 C♯m | A♯m |

| A | F♯ :‖

Verse 1

C♯m C♯11 C♯m   A♯m   A
          I can prove anything, ____

        F♯
I'll make you admit again and again.

C♯m C♯11 C♯m   A♯m   A
      That I can prove anything, ____

        F♯
The way that it's writ again and again.

Chorus 1

      A♯m   C♯
And it's only 'cause you came here with you brothers too,

     Fm   A♯m
If you came here on your own you'd be dead. ____

               C♯
It's only 'cause you follow what the others do,

       Fm   A♯m
It's no ex - cuse to say you're easily led. ____

© Copyright 2006 Rondor Music (London) Limited.
All rights in Germany administered by Rondor Musikverlag GmbH.
All Rights Reserved. International Copyright Secured.

Verse 2

C#m C#11 C#m   A#m   A
              You could choose anything,____
           F#
And you choose to lose again and again.
C#m C#11 C#m   A#m   A
           And you could do anything,____
           F#
But why should you do anything again?

Chorus 2

      A#m   C#
And it's only 'cause you came here with you brothers too,
     Fm   A#m
If you came here on your own you'd be dead. ____
                         C#
You're winding yourself up until you're turning blue,
     Fm   A#m
Re - peating ev'rything that you've read. ____

Bridge 1

G#   D#m C# G#
    So here we go with the letter:
                 D#m C# B
"Well can you fix it for me,
                 D#m C# B
Because we need entertainment,

To keep us all off the streets."
   C#   D#m   C#   B
So to. - night you'll sleep softly in your beds.

Verse 3

C#m C#11 C#m   A#m   A
           You could try anything,____
           F#
And noone would know apart from you and me.
C#m C#11 C#m   A#m   A
           And you could stop anything,____
           F#
It starts with just one, and turns to two then three.

Chorus 3

A♯m   C♯

It's only 'cause you came here with you brothers too,

      Fm   A♯m

If you came here on your own you'd be dead. ____

                               C♯

You raise a glass or two, you raise a fist or two,

      Fm   A♯m

And get a shopping basket wrapped 'round your head. ____

Bridge 2

G♯   D♯m C♯ G♯

  So here we go with the letter:

                      D♯m C♯ B

"Oh can you fix it for me,

                      D♯m C♯ B

For twenty-four hour drinking,

To keep us all off the streets."

  C♯   D♯m   C♯   B

So to - night you'll sleep softly in your beds.

Interlude   ‖: B5 C♯5 | D5   F♯5 | G5 A5 | F♯5   :‖

Outro

   B5

‖: We are the angry mob,

C♯5   D5   F♯5

We read the papers ev'ry day.

   G5   A5

We like who we like, we hate who we hate,

        F♯5

But we're also easily swayed. :‖ *repeat 8 times*

| B5   C♯5 | D5 F♯5 |

 We are the angry mob.

| G5 A5 | F♯5 | B5   ‖

Autumnsong

Words & Music by
James Dean Bradfield, Nicky Wire & Sean Moore

D5   D   F#m   F#mb6   G

Dsus4   Bm   Em   Asus4   A/C#   D/F#

Intro   ‖ N.C. | N.C. | D5 | D5 ‖
*(with guitar riff)*_____

Verse 1

D   F#m   F#mb6 F#m G
   Wear your eyes as dark as night,

                       D   Dsus4 D Bm
And paint your face with what you like.

                 Em
Wear your love like it is made of hate,

Em   D   Dsus4 D   A Asus4 A D
Born to des - troy and born to   cre - ate._

Pre-chorus 1

                   F#m   F#mb6 F#m G
Now baby, what you done to your hair?

                 D   A/C# Bm
Is it just the same time of year?

                     Em
When you think that you don't really care,

Em   D   Dsus4 D   A
Now baby what have you done to   your hair?_____
                                         (Done to your hair,)

                                                D
Done to your hair, done to your hair, done to your hair?_

Chorus 1

(D)   Em   D/F#
So when you hear this autumnsong,

                    G   D
Clear your heads and get ready to run.

               Em   D/F#
So when you hear this autumnsong,

                         G
Remember the best times are yet to come.

© Copyright 2007 Sony/ATV Music Publishing (UK) Limited.
All Rights Reserved. International Copyright Secured.

Link 1 ‖ D⁵ | D⁵ ‖
(with guitar riff)——

Verse 2

<pre>
 D   F♯m   F♯m♭6 F♯m G
    Now baby, what you done to your hair?
                    D   Dsus⁴ D Bm
   Is it just the same time of year?
                              Em
   When you think that you don't really care,
   Em   D   Dsus⁴ D   A Asus⁴ A D
   Now baby, what have you done to   your hair?—
</pre>

Pre-chorus 2

<pre>
                   F♯m   F♯m♭6 F♯m G
   Wear your eyes as dark as night,
                       D   A/C♯ Bm
   And paint your face with what you like.
                         Em
   Wear your love like it is made of hate,
   Em   D   Dsus⁴ D   A
   Born to des - troy and born to   cre - ate.—
                                    (Born to create,)
                                          D
   Born to create, born to create, born to create.—
</pre>

Chorus 2   As Chorus 1

Bridge

<pre>
 A   Bm   A
    So wear your hair in bunches,
                Bm   A   G
   And your jacket loose.
                       F♯m
   So when you hear this autumnsong,
            Em   G   A
   Clear your heads and get ready to run. —
</pre>

Guitar Solo

‖ D | F♯m | G | D   A/C♯ |

| Bm | Em | D | A |

| A | A | A   ‖

Chorus 3   As Chorus 1

Outro   ‖ D⁵ | D⁵ | D⁵ | D⁵ | D⁵ | D⁵ ‖
(with guitar riff)———————

Books From Boxes

Words & Music by
Paul Smith, Thomas English, Duncan Lloyd, Archis Tiku & Lukas Wooller

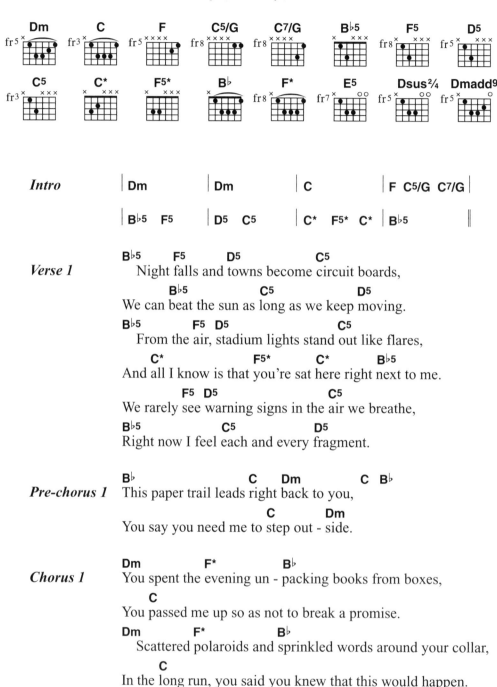

Intro | Dm | Dm | C | F C5/G C7/G |

| B♭5 F5 | D5 C5 | C* F5* C* | B♭5 ‖

Verse 1

B♭5   F5   D5   C5
Night falls and towns become circuit boards,

    B♭5   C5   D5
We can beat the sun as long as we keep moving.

B♭5   F5 D5   C5
From the air, stadium lights stand out like flares,

    C*   F5*   C*   B♭5
And all I know is that you're sat here right next to me.

         F5 D5   C5
We rarely see warning signs in the air we breathe,

B♭5   C5   D5
Right now I feel each and every fragment.

Pre-chorus 1

B♭   C   Dm   C B♭
This paper trail leads right back to you,

                      C   Dm
You say you need me to step out - side.

Chorus 1

Dm   F*   B♭
You spent the evening un - packing books from boxes,

   C
You passed me up so as not to break a promise.

Dm   F*   B♭
Scattered polaroids and sprinkled words around your collar,

   C
In the long run, you said you knew that this would happen.

© Copyright 2007 Universal Music Publishing Limited.
All rights in Germany administered by Universal Music Publ. GmbH.
All Rights Reserved. International Copyright Secured.

Verse 2

B♭5   F5
Well this is something new,

      D5   C5
But it turns out it was borrowed, too.

C*   F5*   C*   B♭5
"Why does every let-down have to be so thin?"

       F5   D5   C5
Rain ex - plodes at the moment that the cab door closed,

   B♭5   C5   D5
I feel the weight up - on your kiss; am - biguous.

Pre-chorus 2

B♭5   C   Dm   C B♭
You have to leave, I ap - preciate that.

                   C   Dm
But I hate when conver - sation slips out of our grasp.

Chorus 2   As Chorus 1

Bridge

‖: E5 | E5 | Dsus²⁄₄ | Dsus²⁄₄ :‖

E5   Dsus²⁄₄
Two bodies in motion, this is a matter of fact, it wasn't built to last.

E5   Dsus²⁄₄
Two bodies in motion, this is a matter of fact, it wasn't built to last.

Chorus 3

Dm   F*   B♭
You spent the evening un - packing books from boxes,

    C
You passed me up so as not to break a promise.

Dm   F*   B♭
Scattered polaroids and sprinkled words around your collar,

     C
In the long run, you said you knew that this would happen.

Dm   F*   B♭
The pounding rain con - tinued its bleak fall,

    C
And we decided just to write after all, after all.

Outro

| B♭5 F5 | D5 C5 | C* F5* C* | B♭5 |

B♭5   F5   D5   C5
The pounding rain con - tinued its bleak fall,

B♭5   C5   Dmadd9
We decided just to write after all.

Down Boy

Words & Music by
Nicholas Zinner, Brian Chase & Karen Orzolek

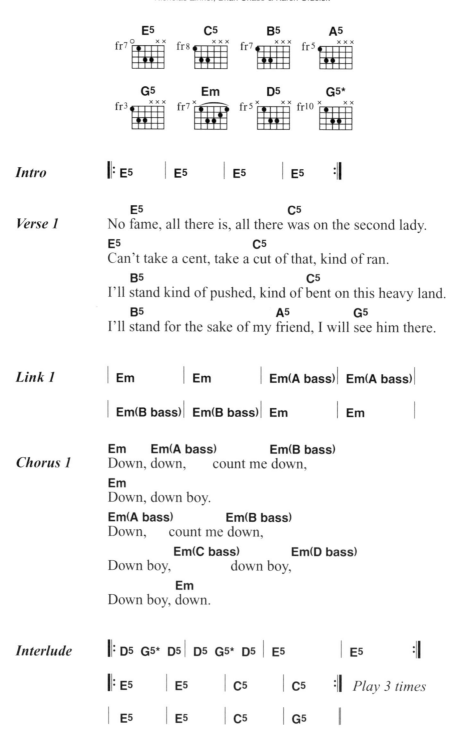

Intro

‖: E5 | E5 | E5 | E5 :‖

Verse 1

E5   C5
No fame, all there is, all there was on the second lady.
E5   C5
Can't take a cent, take a cut of that, kind of ran.
     B5   C5
I'll stand kind of pushed, kind of bent on this heavy land.
     B5   A5   G5
I'll stand for the sake of my friend, I will see him there.

Link 1

| Em | Em | Em(A bass) | Em(A bass) |

| Em(B bass) | Em(B bass) | Em | Em | |

Chorus 1

Em   Em(A bass)   Em(B bass)
Down, down,   count me down,
Em
Down, down boy.
Em(A bass)   Em(B bass)
Down,   count me down,
       Em(C bass)   Em(D bass)
Down boy,   down boy,
       Em
Down boy, down.

Interlude

‖: D5 G5* D5 | D5 G5* D5 | E5 | E5 :‖

‖: E5 | E5 | C5 | C5 :‖ *Play 3 times*

| E5 | E5 | C5 | G5 |

© Copyright 2003 Chrysalis Music Limited.
All Rights Reserved. International Copyright Secured.

14

Verse 2

      E5   G5   C5   D5
The same, not begin, not give up, in a better way.

      E5   G5   C5   D5
A - gain, wash the stain off his bed, not to split them up.

      B5   C5
I'll stand for the sake of my friend,

               D5   B5   A5
I will see him there,   well, I will see him there.

Link 2

| Em | Em | Em(A bass) | Em(A bass) |

| Em(B bass) | Em(B bass) | Em | Em | |

Chorus 2

Em   Em(A bass)   Em(B bass)
Down, down,   count me down,

Em
Down, down boy.

Em(A bass)   Em(B bass)
Down,   count me down,

           Em(C bass)   Em(D bass)
Down boy,   down boy,

           Em
Down boy, down.

Em(A bass)   Em(B bass)
Down,   count me down,

Em
Down, down boy.

Outro

||: D5 G5* D5 | D5 G5* D5 | E5 | E5 :||

||: E5 | E5 | C5 | C5 :|| *Play 3 times*

| E5 | E5 | C5 | G5 |

| E5 ||

Dream Catch Me

Words & Music by
Crispin Hunt, Gordon Mills & Newton Faulkner

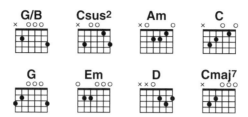

Capo seventh fret

Intro

| N.C. | N.C. | G/B | G/B ‖

Verse 1

G/B   Csus2 G/B   Csus2
Eve - ry time   I close my   eyes,

      Am   C   G   Em
It's you and I know now who I   am.

         Am
Yeah, yeah, yeah,

        D
And I know now.

Pre-chorus 1

    G   D
  There's a place I go when I'm a - lone,

                          Em
Do anything I want, be anyone I wanna be.

                      C   G
But it is us I see and I cannot believe I'm falling.

                                         D
That's where I'm going, where are you go - ing?

                     Em
Hold it close, won't let this go.

Chorus 1

               Cmaj7
Dream catch me, yeah,

                   Am   Cmaj7
Dream catch me when I fall,

                       G/B
Or else I won't come back at all.

© Copyright 2007 Universal Music Publishing Limited (45%)/Peermusic (UK) Limited (35%)/
Outcaste Music Publishing Limited (20%).
All rights in Germany administered by Universal Music Publ. GmbH.
All Rights Reserved. International Copyright Secured.

Verse 2

```
      Csus²   G/B                Csus²
You do so much     that you don't         know,
     Am          C           Em    G
It's true and I know now who I     am.
             Am
Yeah, yeah, yeah,
             D
And I know now.
```

Pre-chorus 2   As Pre-chorus 1

Chorus 2

```
      Em                   Cmaj⁷
Dream catch me, yeah,
                     Am    Cmaj⁷
Dream catch me when I fall,
                          Em
Or else I won't come back at all.
```

Bridge

```
               C                   G
See you as a mountain, a fountain of God,
                 D            Em
See you as a descant soul in the setting sun.
             C                   G
Nuance of sound has decided it's love,
D
I'm young.
```

Pre-chorus 3

```
      G                         D
    There's a place I go when I'm a - lone,
                               Em
Do anything I want, be anyone I wanna be.
                    C
But it is us I see and I cannot believe I'm falling.
```

Pre-chorus 4   As Pre-chorus 1

Chorus 3

```
      Em                   Cmaj⁷
Dream catch me, yeah,
                     Am    Cmaj⁷
Dream catch me when I fall,
                          G
Or else I won't come back at all.
```

Direct Hit

Words & Music by
Ian Wilson, Eddie Argos, Michael Breyer, Jasper Fulcher & Friederike Siepe

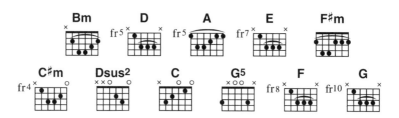

Intro

‖: Bm | Bm | D | A :‖

| Bm | Bm | D | E F#m | F#m ‖

Verse 1

C#m   Dsus2
   You went out in a rush,
     C   G5
And can't tell if it shows.
C#m   Dsus2
She's looking over a lot,
     C   G5
And he's still in his work clothes.

Pre-chorus 1

      C#m   D
You can't talk to members of the   opposite sex,
         F   G
He starts to talk, they start to   look perplexed.
         C#m   D
So with his eyes on the prize, and just a   glance at her breasts,
         G   N.C.
He walks over,   and he says:

Chorus 1

Bm   D
   "It's uncomfortable all night to sit,
              A   Bm
Get on the dancefloor, it's a direct hit.
                 D
Move around like your shoes don't fit,
              E   F#m Bm
Get on the dancefloor, it's a direct hit.

© Copyright 2006 Reverb Music Limited.
All Rights Reserved. International Copyright Secured.

                    D
Why is that cigarette unlit?
               A   **Bm**
Get on the dancefloor, it's a direct hit.
                  D
What's wrong? Scared to commit?
            E   **F♯m**
Get on the dancefloor, it's a direct hit."

Verse 2

C♯m   **Dsus2**
Her friends are leaving,
        C   **G5**
She decides she's not going.
C♯m   **Dsus2**
She's been looking over a lot,
         C   **G5**
And hopes it's been showing.

Pre-chorus 2

C♯m   **D**
She can't talk to members of the   opposite sex,
        F   **G**
She starts to talk, they start to   look perplexed.
            C♯m   **D**
So with her eyes on the prize, and just a   glance at her breasts,
F   **G**   **N.C.**
She goes over, and she says:

Chorus 2

Bm   **D**
"It's uncomfortable all night to sit,
               A   **Bm**
Get on the dancefloor, it's a direct hit.
                      D
Move around like your shoes don't fit,
               E   **F♯m** **Bm**
Get on the dancefloor, it's a direct hit.
                  D
What's wrong? Scared to commit?
               A   **Bm**
Get on the dancefloor, it's a direct hit,
                      D
I don't care that your friends have split,
               E   **F♯m**
Get on the dancefloor, it's a direct hit."

Interlude | C♯m | Dsus2 | C | G5 |

                 | C♯m | D | F | G | N.C. | N.C.   ‖

Chorus 3

```
Bm                              D
    Here comes the really good bit,
                     A          Bm
Get on the dancefloor, it's a direct hit.
                                 D
Move around like your shoes don't fit,
                     A          Bm
Get on the dancefloor, it's a direct hit.
                               D
It's uncomfortable all night to sit,
                     A          Bm
Get on the dancefloor, it's a direct hit.
                            D
Why is that cigarette unlit?
                     E          F♯m
Get on the dancefloor, it's a direct hit.
```

Chorus 4

```
Bm                                         D
    I don't care that your friends have split,
                     A          Bm
Get on the dancefloor, it's a direct hit.
                                 D
Move around like your shoes don't fit,
                     E    F♯m  Bm
Get on the dancefloor, it's a direct hit.
                               D
What's wrong? Scared to commit?
                     A          Bm
Get on the dancefloor, it's a direct hit.
                               D
It's uncomfortable all night to sit,
                     E          F♯m
Get on the dancefloor, it's a direct hit.
```

Outro

```
Bm
Hit, hit, direct hit.
D       A
Hit, hit, direct hit.
Bm
Hit, hit, direct hit.
D       E     F♯m  Bm
Hit, hit, direct hit.
```

Everything Is Average Nowadays

Words & Music by
Charlie Wilson, Nicholas Hodgson, Andrew White, James Rix & Nicholas Baines

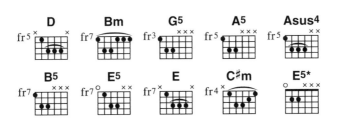

Intro | D | D   ‖

Chorus 1
     D   **Bm**
So, ev'rything is av'rage nowa - days

                     D
Ev'rything is av'rage nowa - days.

                    Bm
But ev'ryone would do it if they can,

                  G5
And ev'rything is going down the pan.

               A5
And ev'ryone is following the craze,

Of ev'rything is av'rage now.

Verse 1
     D
You say it's getting better,

 Bm
But I don't really see the signs.

  D
You say it is too diff'rent,

  Bm
You thought it would be suicide.

Pre-chorus 1
    G5
There's not much to believe in,

A5
Left up on the shelf.

  G5
So get your coat we're leaving,

   A5   **Asus4**
We'll just do something else._____

© Copyright 2006 Rondor Music (London) Limited.
All rights in Germany administered by Rondor Musikverlag GmbH.
All Rights Reserved. International Copyright Secured.

Chorus 2
     D   **Bm**
Oh, ev'rything is av'rage nowa - days

                       D
Ev'rything is av'rage nowa - days.

                    Bm
But ev'rything is of no conse - quence,

                     G5
'Cause ev'ryone is sitting on the fence.

                        A5
And ev'rything will always stay the same,

'Cause ev'rything is av'rage now.

Verse 2
     D
You say we didn't need it,

     Bm
You threw away the book of rules.

     D
You thought that we should read it,

     Bm
I wouldn't even know how to.

Pre-chorus 2   As Pre-chorus 1

Bridge
B5   **E5**
All I need is a ball and a wall,

     A5   **G5**   **A5**
Or a sledge and a hill in heavy weather.

B5   **E5**
All I need is a ball and a wall,

     A5   **G5**   **A5**
A sledge and a hill in heavy weather.

B5
Oh, oh, oh, oh. Oh, oh, oh, oh. Oh....

Link   ‖: D | D | Bm | Bm   :‖

Pre-chorus 3

G⁵
Not much to believe in,

A⁵
Left up on the shelf.

    G⁵
So get your coat we're leaving,

   A⁵   **Asus⁴**
We'll just do something else._____

    E   **C♯m**
Chorus 3   Oh, ev'rything is av'rage nowa - days

                     E
Ev'rything is av'rage nowa - days.

                       C♯m
When ev'ryone would do it if they can,

                   A⁵
And ev'rything is going down the pan.

                 B⁵
And ev'ryone is following the craze,

                 E⁵*
Of ev'rything is av'rage nowa - days.

Fans

Words & Music by
Caleb Followill, Nathan Followill, Jared Followill & Matthew Followill

E   Aadd⁹/E   Badd¹¹/E
                  fr6   fr8

Intro   ‖ E | E | |

‖: E   Aadd⁹/E | Badd¹¹/E Aadd⁹/E |

| E   Aadd⁹/E | Badd¹¹/E Aadd⁹/E :‖

2° (Home-)

Verse 1
E
Home - grown.
Aadd⁹/E   Badd¹¹/E Aadd⁹/E   E
Rock to the rhythm and bop to the beat of the ra - dio.
Aadd⁹/E   Badd¹¹/E Aadd⁹/E E
You ain't got the slang but you got the face to   play the role.
           Aadd⁹/E   Badd¹¹/E Aadd⁹/E E Aadd⁹/E Badd¹¹/E
And you can play with me._____

Verse 2
E
And all the bro's,
Aadd⁹/E   Badd¹¹/E Aadd⁹/E E
Try for the courage and try for   charity's tight clothes.
Aadd⁹/E   Badd¹¹/E Aadd⁹/E   E
She's got a hat and all the   hat says is asshole,
Aadd⁹/E   Badd¹¹/E Aadd⁹/E E Aadd⁹/E Badd¹¹/E
She'll be bobbing to me._____

Chorus 1
Aadd⁹/E   E
Pretty hairdos,
           Aadd⁹/E   Badd¹¹/E   Aadd⁹/E E
And those lipstick kisses blown yeah that's the right move.
Aadd⁹/E   Badd¹¹/E   Aadd⁹/E E
Make me feel like I'm the one who   moves you,
           Aadd⁹/E   Badd¹¹/E Aadd⁹/E E Aadd⁹/E Badd¹¹/E
The only one you see. _____

Verse 3
E
Now take it down.
Aadd⁹/E   Badd¹¹/E   Aadd⁹/E   E
Don't you let those tears quench the   thirs - ty ground.

© Copyright 2007 Martha Street Music/Followill Music/Songs Of Combustion Music/
McFearless Music/Coffee Tea Or Me Publishing, USA.
Bug Music Limited (45%)/P & P Songs Limited (55%).
All Rights Reserved. International Copyright Secured.

cont.

Aadd⁹/E   Badd¹¹/E   Aadd⁹/E   E

Don't you be so scared that you   can't make a sound.

Aadd⁹/E   Badd¹¹/E   Aadd⁹/E   E   Aadd⁹/E   Badd¹¹/E

Make a sound for me. _____

Chorus 2

Aadd⁹/E   E

   All of London sing,

     Aadd⁹/E   Badd¹¹/E   Aadd⁹/E   E

'Cause England swings and they sure love the tales   I bring.

      Aadd⁹/E   Badd¹¹/E   Aadd⁹/E   E

And those rainy days they ain't so bad when you're   the king,

     Aadd⁹/E   Badd¹¹/E   Aadd⁹/E   E

The king they want to see. _____

| Aadd⁹/E   Badd¹¹/E   Aadd⁹/E ‖

Guitar Solo

‖:   E   Aadd⁹/E | Badd¹¹/E   Aadd⁹/E |

| E   Aadd⁹/E | Badd¹¹/E   Aadd⁹/E :‖

                         2ᵒ (Home-)

Verse 4

As Verse 1

Chorus 3

Aadd⁹/E   E

Pretty hair - dos,

     Aadd⁹/E   Badd¹¹/E   Aadd⁹/E   E

And those lipstick kisses blown yeah that's the right move.

Aadd⁹/E   Badd¹¹/E   Aadd⁹/E   E

Make me feel like I'm the one who's mov - in' you,

     Aadd⁹/E   Badd¹¹/E   Aadd⁹/E   E   Aadd⁹/E   Badd¹¹/E

The only one you see. _____

Chorus 4

As Chorus 2

Outro

‖:   E   Aadd⁹/E | Badd¹¹/E   Aadd⁹/E |

| E   Aadd⁹/E | Badd¹¹/E   Aadd⁹/E :‖   E   ‖

For Reasons Unknown

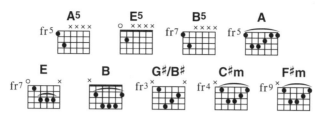

Words & Music by
Brandon Flowers, Dave Keuning, Mark Stoermer & Ronnie Vannucci

Tune guitar down a semitone

Verse 1

      A5   E5
I pack my case, I check my face, I look a little bit older.

                  B5
I look a little bit colder.

         A5   E5
With one deep breath and one big step, I move a little bit closer.

                 B5
I move a little bit closer.

         A5
For reasons unknown.

Verse 2

         A
I caught my stride, I flew and flied.

        E   B   G♯/B♯
I know if destiny's kind, I've got the rest on my mind.

      C♯m   A
But my heart, it don't beat, it don't beat the way it used to,

        E   B   G♯/B♯
And my eyes, they don't see you no more. _____

      C♯m   A
And my lips, they don't kiss, they don't kiss the way they used to,

        E   B   G♯/B♯
And my eyes don't recognise you no more. _____

Chorus 1

        E   F♯m   C♯m B
For reasons un - known,

        E   F♯m   C♯m B
For reasons un - known.

© Copyright 2006 Universal Music Publishing Limited.
All rights in Germany administered by Universal Music Publ. GmbH.
All Rights Reserved. International Copyright Secured.

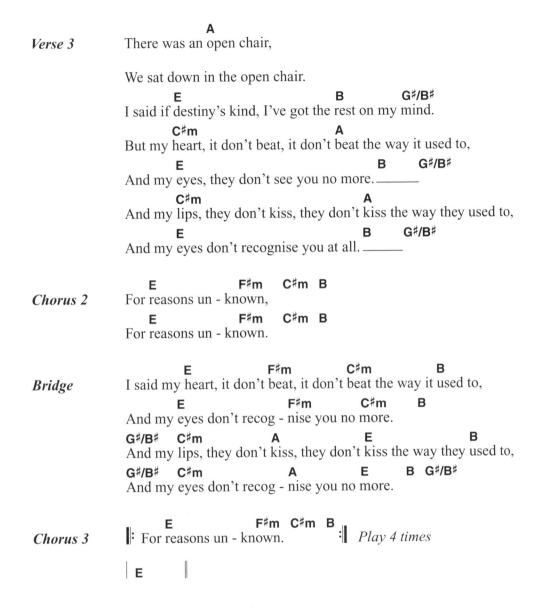

Verse 3

               A
There was an open chair,

We sat down in the open chair.
      E   **B**   **G♯/B♯**
I said if destiny's kind, I've got the rest on my mind.
      C♯m   **A**
But my heart, it don't beat, it don't beat the way it used to,
      E   **B**   **G♯/B♯**
And my eyes, they don't see you no more. _____
      C♯m   **A**
And my lips, they don't kiss, they don't kiss the way they used to,
      E   **B**   **G♯/B♯**
And my eyes don't recognise you at all. _____

Chorus 2

      E   **F♯m**   **C♯m** **B**
For reasons un - known,
      E   **F♯m**   **C♯m** **B**
For reasons un - known.

Bridge

      E   **F♯m**   **C♯m**   **B**
I said my heart, it don't beat, it don't beat the way it used to,
      E   **F♯m**   **C♯m**   **B**
And my eyes don't recog - nise you no more.
G♯/B♯   **C♯m**   **A**   **E**   **B**
And my lips, they don't kiss, they don't kiss the way they used to,
G♯/B♯   **C♯m**   **A**   **E**   **B** **G♯/B♯**
And my eyes don't recog - nise you no more.

Chorus 3

        E   **F♯m** **C♯m** **B**
‖: For reasons un - known.   :‖ *Play 4 times*

   | **E**   ‖

Foundations

Words & Music by
Kate Nash & Paul Epworth

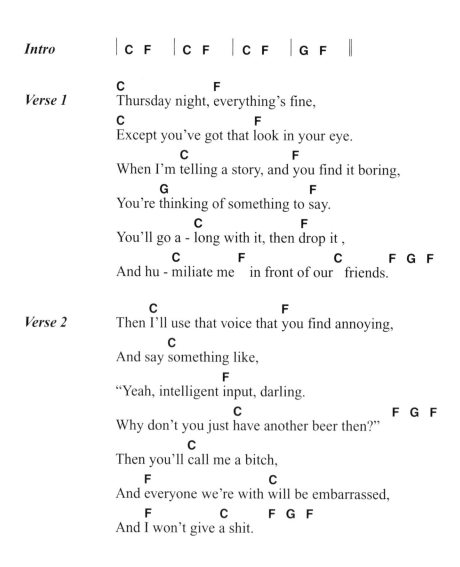

Intro | C F | C F | C F | G F ‖

Verse 1
```
     C                   F
Thursday night, everything's fine,
     C                   F
Except you've got that look in your eye.
          C                 F
When I'm telling a story, and you find it boring,
        G                   F
You're thinking of something to say.
               C             F
You'll go a - long with it, then drop it ,
          C        F          C      F G  F
And hu - miliate me   in front of our   friends.
```

Verse 2
```
          C                    F
Then I'll use that voice that you find annoying,
          C
And say something like,
               F
"Yeah, intelligent input, darling.
                   C                   F G  F
Why don't you just have another beer then?"
          C
Then you'll call me a bitch,
       F                 C
And everyone we're with will be embarrassed,
       F        C      F G  F
And I won't give a shit.
```

© Copyright 2007 Universal Music Publishing Limited (62.5%)/EMI Music Publishing Limited (37.5%).
All rights in Germany administered by Universal Music Publ. GmbH.
All Rights Reserved. International Copyright Secured.

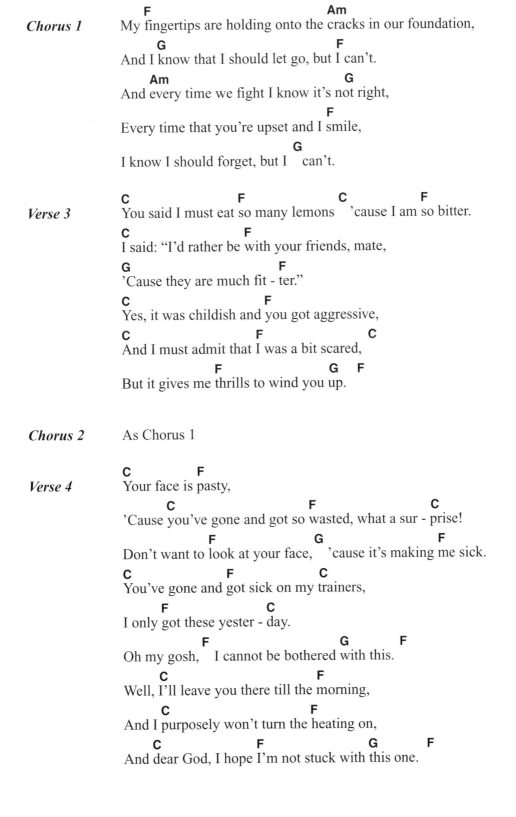

Chorus 1

F   Am
My fingertips are holding onto the cracks in our foundation,
        G   F
And I know that I should let go, but I can't.
      Am   G
And every time we fight I know it's not right,
                                  F
Every time that you're upset and I smile,
                          G
I know I should forget, but I   can't.

Verse 3

    C   F   C   F
You said I must eat so many lemons   'cause I am so bitter.
    C   F
I said: "I'd rather be with your friends, mate,
    G   F
'Cause they are much fit - ter."
    C   F
Yes, it was childish and you got aggressive,
    C   F   C
And I must admit that I was a bit scared,
                  F   G   F
But it gives me thrills to wind you up.

Chorus 2   As Chorus 1

Verse 4

    C   F
Your face is pasty,
        C   F   C
'Cause you've gone and got so wasted, what a sur - prise!
         F   G   F
Don't want to look at your face,   'cause it's making me sick.
    C   F   C
You've gone and got sick on my trainers,
        F   C
I only got these yester - day.
            F   G   F
Oh my gosh,   I cannot be bothered with this.
      C   F
Well, I'll leave you there till the morning,
      C   F
And I purposely won't turn the heating on,
      C   F   G   F
And dear God, I hope I'm not stuck with this one.

Chorus 3   As Chorus 1

            F   **Am**

Chorus 4

                       F

      And every time we fight I know it's not right,   **Am**

                                        G

      Every time that you're upset and I smile,

                             F

      I know I should forget, but I can't.

            Am   **G**

      And every time we fight I know it's not right,

                                F

      Every time that you're upset and I smile,

                             G

      I know I should forget, but I   can't.

Outro | F | Am | G | F |

               | Am | G | F | G | Am   ‖

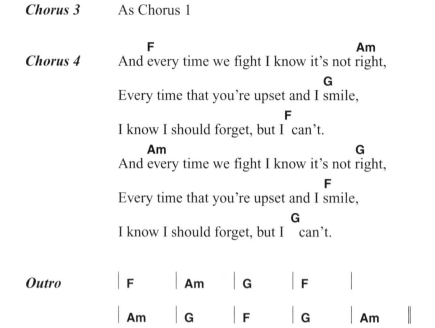

Guitar

Words & Music by
Prince

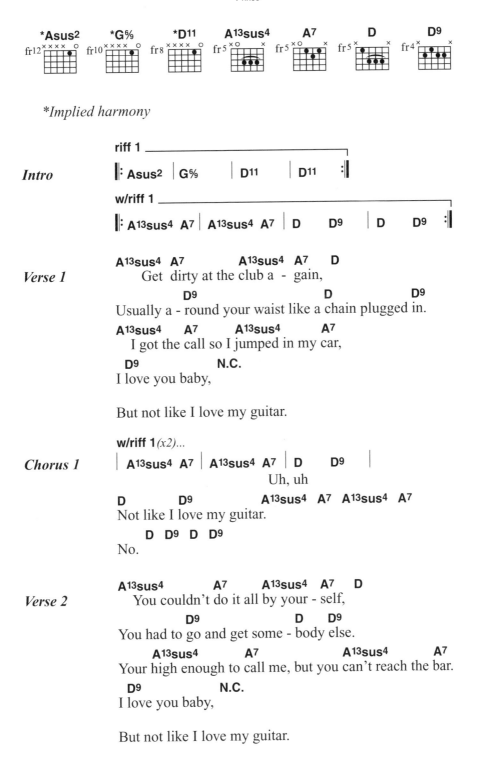

*Implied harmony

Intro

riff 1 _____

‖: Asus² | G% | D11 | D11 :‖

w/riff 1 _____

‖: A¹³sus⁴ A⁷ | A¹³sus⁴ A⁷ | D　D⁹ | D　D⁹ :‖

Verse 1

A¹³sus⁴　A⁷　　　　A¹³sus⁴　A⁷　　D
　Get dirty at the club a - gain,
　　　　　D⁹　　　　　　　　　D　　　　D⁹
Usually a - round your waist like a chain plugged in.
A¹³sus⁴　　A⁷　　　A¹³sus⁴　　A⁷
　I got the call so I jumped in my car,
D⁹　　　　　　　N.C.
I love you baby,

But not like I love my guitar.

Chorus 1

w/riff 1 (x2)...
| A¹³sus⁴ A⁷ | A¹³sus⁴ A⁷ | D　D⁹ |
　　　　　　　　　　　　　Uh, uh
D　　　D⁹　　　　　A¹³sus⁴　A⁷　A¹³sus⁴　A⁷
Not like I love my guitar.
　　　D　D⁹　D　D⁹
No.

Verse 2

A¹³sus⁴　　　　A⁷　　　A¹³sus⁴　A⁷　D
　You couldn't do it all by your - self,
　　　　　　D⁹　　　　　　　D　　D⁹
You had to go and get some - body else.
　　　A¹³sus⁴　　　A⁷　　　A¹³sus⁴　　　A⁷
Your high enough to call me, but you can't reach the bar.
　　D⁹　　　　　　　N.C.
I love you baby,

But not like I love my guitar.

© Copyright 2007 Controversy Music/Universal Music Corporation, USA.
Universal/MCA Music Limited. All rights in Germany administered by Universal/MCA Music Publ. GmbH.
All Rights Reserved. International Copyright Secured.

w/riff 1 *(x2)...*

Chorus 2 | A¹³sus⁴ A⁷ | A¹³sus⁴ A⁷ | D   D⁹ |

          No,

D   D⁹   A¹³sus⁴ A⁷ A¹³sus⁴
Not like I love my gui - tar.

   A⁷ D D⁹ D D⁹
Oh just turn it up.

Solo ‖: A⁷ | A⁷ | D⁹ | D⁹ :‖ *Play 4 times*

Interlude | Asus² | G⁶⁄₉ | D¹¹ | D¹¹ ‖

Verse 3

A¹³sus⁴   A⁷   A¹³sus⁴ A⁷ D
   I tried to warn you that its hard to be a star,

     D⁹   D   D⁹
Especially when your driving other peo - ple's car.

     A¹³sus⁴ A⁷   A¹³sus⁴ A⁷
Would of gave you mine girl, but you took it too far.

 D⁹   N.C.
I love you baby,

Just not like I love my guitar.

w/riff 1 *(x2)...*

| A¹³sus⁴ A⁷ |

A¹³sus⁴ A⁷
Wow.

Chorus 3

    D D⁹
Uh, uh.

D   D⁹   A¹³sus⁴ A⁷ A¹³sus⁴
Not like I love my guitar.

A⁷ D D⁹ D D⁹
Oh.

Verse 4

A¹³sus⁴   A⁷   A¹³sus⁴   A⁷   D
> I know you love me and you want to be friends,

          D⁹   D   D⁹
And if you don't at least you need to pre - tend.

A¹³sus⁴   A⁷   A¹³sus⁴   A⁷
  We're still to - gether, even if we don't get that far,

    D⁹   N.C.
I love you baby,

But not like I love this guitar.

Chorus 4

w/riff 1 *(x2)*...

| A¹³sus⁴ A⁷ A¹³sus⁴ A⁷ |

D   D⁹
I love you baby, I love you baby,

D   D⁹
Not like I love my guitar.

Outro

w/riff 1 *(x2)*...

A¹³sus⁴   A⁷   A¹³sus⁴ A⁷   D
I love you baby and I wish you well,

           D⁹   D   D⁹
I'll write a letter when I learn how to spell.

A¹³sus⁴   A⁷   A¹³sus⁴   A⁷
  Until the day you can go to...

D⁹
  I love you baby, you know the rest.

Outro solo   ‖: A⁷ | A⁷ | D⁹ | D⁹ :‖ *Play 4 times to fade*

Green Fields

Words & Music by
Damon Albarn & Paul Simonon

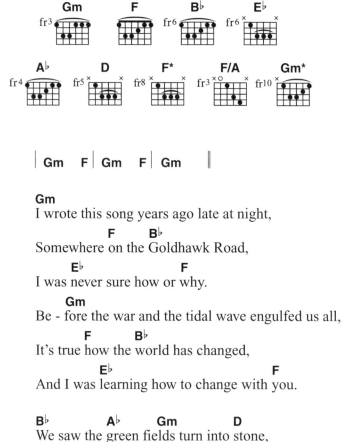

Intro | Gm   F | Gm   F | Gm   ‖

Verse 1

Gm
I wrote this song years ago late at night,
     F   **B♭**
Somewhere on the Goldhawk Road,
     E♭   **F**
I was never sure how or why.
     Gm
Be - fore the war and the tidal wave engulfed us all,
     F   **B♭**
It's true how the world has changed,
     E♭   **F**
And I was learning how to change with you.

Chorus 1

B♭   **A♭**   **Gm**   **D**
We saw the green fields turn into stone,
          E♭   **F***
Such lonely homes.
B♭   **A♭**   **Gm**
All in the badman dream,
          D   **E♭**   **F***
He ain't a - wake, he's a dream.

Link 1 | Gm | Gm   ‖

© Copyright 2007 Chrysalis Music Limited
All Rights Reserved. International Copyright Secured.

Verse 2

Gm
In the darkest hour the song had gone,
                              F/A B♭
It passed among people   I hardly knew,
        E♭   F*
I was losing it all the time.
        Gm
She stayed with me and found me out,

And above all things I've learnt
F/A   B♭   E♭   F*
It's the honesty that se - cures the bond in the heart.

Chorus 2

B♭   A♭   Gm   D
We saw the green fields turn into stone,
                    E♭   F*
Such lonely homes.
B♭   A♭   Gm
All in the badman dream,
                D   E♭   F*
He ain't a - wake, he's a dream.

Outro

| Gm* | B♭ | E♭ | F* |
(w/vocals ad lib)
| Gm* F*| D E♭ | F* | B♭   ‖

35

Hospital Beds

Words & Music by
Nathan Willett, Matthew Maust, Jonathan Russell & Matthew Aveiro

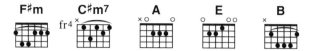

Intro

| F♯m C♯m7 | A E | F♯m C♯m7 | A E |

| F♯m C♯m7 | A E | F♯m C♯m7 | A E ‖

Verse 1

F♯m　　　　C♯m7　　　　　　　　A　　　　　　　E
There's nothing to do here, some just whine and com - plain,
F♯m　　C♯m7　　A E
In bed at the hospital.
F♯m　　　　C♯m7　　　A　　　　　E
Coming and going, a - sleep and a - wake,
　F♯m　　　　C♯m7　　A E
In bed at the hospital.

Link 1

| F♯m C♯m7 | A E ‖

Verse 2

F♯m　　　C♯m7　　　　　　A　　　E
Tell me the story of how you ended up here,
　　　　F♯m　　C♯m7　　A E
I've heard it all in the hospital.
F♯m　　　C♯m7　A　　　　E
Nurses are fussing, doctor's on tour,
F♯m　　　　C♯m7　A E
Somewhere in India.

© Copyright 2006 Universal Music Publishing Limited.
All rights in Germany administered by Universal Music Publ. GmbH.
All Rights Reserved. International Copyright Secured.

Chorus 1

```
        F♯m     C♯m7              A           E
I've got one friend laying a - cross from me,
        F♯m         C♯m7      A         E
I did not choose him, he did not choose me.
          F♯m   C♯m7        A      E      F♯m   C♯m7
We've got no chance of re - cover - y sharing hospi - tal,
    A         E
Joy and miser - y,
      F♯m           C♯m7
Joy and miser - y,
    A            E
Joy and miser - y.
```

Link 2

```
| C♯m7   B | E        | C♯m7   B | E              ‖
```

Bridge 1

```
C♯m7                B     E
Put out the fire boys, don't stop, don't stop,
C♯m7           B  E
Put out the fire on us.
C♯m7                B     E
Put out the fire boys, don't stop, don't stop,
C♯m7             B  E
Put out the fire on us.
              C♯m7
Bring the buckets by the dozens,
B          E
Bring your nieces and your cousins,
      C♯m7          B  E
Come put out the fire on us.
```

Link 3

```
| F♯m C♯m7 | A   E     | F♯m C♯m7 | A    E       ‖
F♯m  C♯m7 A      E    F♯m    C♯m7   A  E
Viet - nam, fishing trips, Italian opera.
F♯m  C♯m7 A      E    F♯m    C♯m7   A  E
Viet - nam, fishing trips, Italian opera.
```

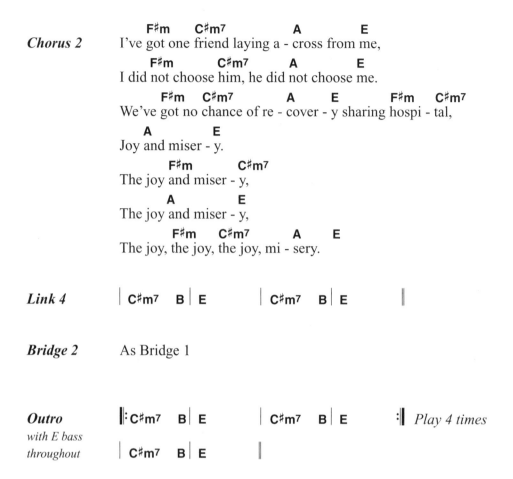

Chorus 2
        F♯m   C♯m⁷   A   E
I've got one friend laying a - cross from me,
        F♯m   C♯m⁷   A   E
I did not choose him, he did not choose me.
          F♯m C♯m⁷   A   E   F♯m   C♯m⁷
We've got no chance of re - cover - y sharing hospi - tal,
      A   E
Joy and miser - y.
         F♯m   C♯m⁷
The joy and miser - y,
         A   E
The joy and miser - y,
         F♯m   C♯m⁷   A   E
The joy, the joy, the joy, mi - sery.

Link 4 | C♯m⁷ B | E | C♯m⁷ B | E   ‖

Bridge 2   As Bridge 1

Outro   ‖: C♯m⁷ B | E | C♯m⁷ B | E   :‖ *Play 4 times*
with E bass
throughout | C♯m⁷ B | E   ‖

I Can't Stop This Feeling I've Got

Words & Music by
Johnny Borrell & Bjorn Agren

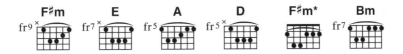

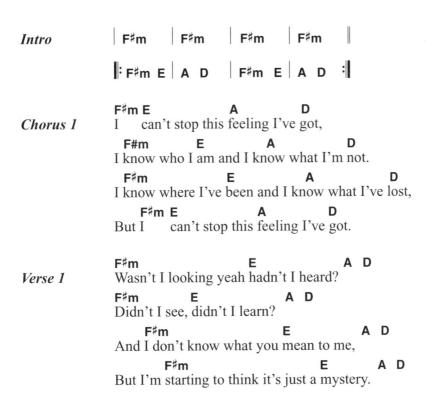

Intro
| F♯m | F♯m | F♯m | F♯m ‖

‖: F♯m E | A D | F♯m E | A D :‖

Chorus 1

F♯m E   A   D
I   can't stop this feeling I've got,

   F#m   E   A   D
I know who I am and I know what I'm not.

   F#m   E   A   D
I know where I've been and I know what I've lost,

    F♯m E   A   D
But I   can't stop this feeling I've got.

Verse 1

   F♯m   E   A   D
Wasn't I looking yeah hadn't I heard?

F♯m   E   A   D
Didn't I see, didn't I learn?

     F♯m   E   A   D
And I don't know what you mean to me,

       F♯m   E   A   D
But I'm starting to think it's just a mystery.

© Copyright 2006 Sony/ATV Music Publishing (UK) Limited
All Rights Reserved. International Copyright Secured.

Chorus 2

```
        F♯m E           A         D
And I     can't stop this feeling I've got,
    F♯m        E        A          D
I know who I am and I know what I'm not.
    F♯m          E          A           D
I know what I've gained and I know what I've lost,
      F♯m E          A         D
But I     can't stop this feeling I've got.
```

Verse 2

```
F♯m                E            A D
Wasn't I looking yeah hadn't I heard?
F♯m      E          A D
Didn't I see, didn't I learn?
  F♯m             E      A D
I may be right you may disagree,
        F♯m                E      A D
But I'm starting to think it's just a mystery.
        F♯m          E      A D
What - ever it is, it's just a mystery.
```

Bridge

```
F♯m*                  Bm
  Are you down oh, when it looks so easy?
D                    A       E
  You spend a lifetime looking for some - one,
F♯m*                 Bm
  And then they come and you're just so uneasy.
D                    A       E
  You get the feeling that the fire don't come,
      D          E
When it's one more story on your way.
```

Chorus 3

```
    F♯m E          A         D
And I     can't stop this feeling I've got,
    F♯m      E      A          D
I know who I am and I know what I'm not.
    F♯m          E        A          D
I know where I've been and I know what I've lost,
      F♯m E      A         D
But I     can't stop this feeling I've got.
```

Verse 3

   F♯m   E   A D
The sky may fall, the sea may split,

F♯m   E   A D
You may say that isn't it.

 F♯m   E   A D
I may be right you may disagree,

F♯m   E   A D
Same old story, same old me.

  F♯m   E   A D
And I don't know what you mean to me,

   F♯m   E   A D
But I'm starting to think it's just a mystery.

  F♯m   E   A D
I've got to admit it's just a mystery.

Outro

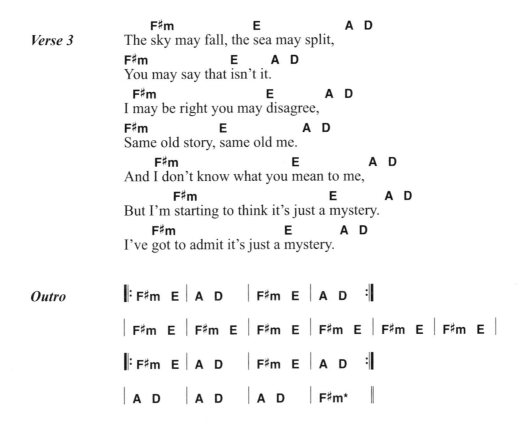

‖: F♯m E | A D | F♯m E | A D :‖

| F♯m E | F♯m E | F♯m E | F♯m E | F♯m E | F♯m E |

‖: F♯m E | A D | F♯m E | A D :‖

| A D | A D | A D | F♯m* ‖

I'm Not Sorry

Words & Music by
Oliver Main & Matthew Bowman

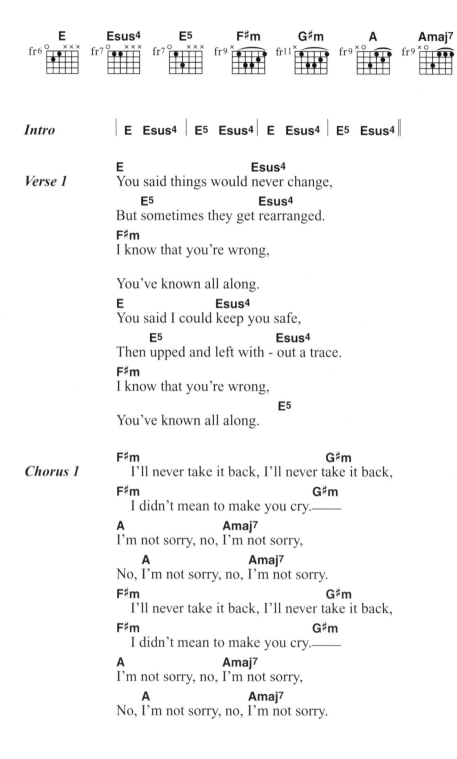

Intro | E Esus⁴ | E⁵ Esus⁴ | E Esus⁴ | E⁵ Esus⁴ ‖

Verse 1

       E   Esus⁴
You said things would never change,

       E⁵   Esus⁴
But sometimes they get rearranged.

F♯m
I know that you're wrong,

You've known all along.

       E   Esus⁴
You said I could keep you safe,

       E⁵   Esus⁴
Then upped and left with - out a trace.

F♯m
I know that you're wrong,

                    E⁵
You've known all along.

Chorus 1

F♯m   G♯m
I'll never take it back, I'll never take it back,

F♯m   G♯m
I didn't mean to make you cry.———

A   Amaj⁷
I'm not sorry, no, I'm not sorry,

    A   Amaj⁷
No, I'm not sorry, no, I'm not sorry.

F♯m   G♯m
I'll never take it back, I'll never take it back,

F♯m   G♯m
I didn't mean to make you cry.———

A   Amaj⁷
I'm not sorry, no, I'm not sorry,

    A   Amaj⁷
No, I'm not sorry, no, I'm not sorry.

© Copyright 2007 BMG Music Publishing Limited.
All Rights Reserved. International Copyright Secured.

Link 1   ‖ E Esus⁴ | E⁵ Esus⁴| E Esus⁴ | E⁵ Esus⁴‖

Verse 2

E   Esus⁴
Things you say, they sound so fake,

    E⁵   Esus⁴
Can make me drink un - til I ache.

F♯m
I know that you're wrong,

You've known all along.

E   Esus⁴
You're not pleased till you draw blood,

    E⁵   Esus⁴
I don't hit back but I think I should.

F♯m
I know that you're wrong,

                              E⁵
You've known all along.

Chorus 2   As Chorus 1

Interlude   ‖ E Esus⁴ | E⁵ Esus⁴| E Esus⁴ | E⁵ Esus⁴‖

Chorus 3   As Chorus 1

Outro | F♯m | F♯m G♯m| F♯m | F♯m G♯m|

           | A | Amaj⁷ | A | Amaj⁷ |

           | F♯m | F♯m G♯m| F♯m | F♯m G♯m| A   ‖

It's Not Over Yet

Words & Music by
Paul Oakenfold, Robert Davis & Michael Wyzgowski

A   F♯m   C♯m   fr4 A*   fr2 Amaj⁷

Intro ‖: A | A | A | A :‖

Verse 1
    A   F♯m   C♯m
I'll live for you, I'd die for you,
    A   F♯m   C♯m
Do what you want me to.
    A   F♯m   C♯m
I'll cry for you, my tears will show,
     A   F♯m   C♯m
That I can't let you go.

Link 1 ‖: A | F♯m | C♯m | C♯m :‖

Chorus 1
        A   F♯m   C♯m
It's not over, not over, not over, not over yet,

But you still want me, don't you?
        A   F♯m   C♯m
It's not over, not over, not over, not over yet,

'Cause I can see through you.
        A   F♯m   C♯m
It's not over, not over, not over, not over yet,

But you still want me, don't you?
        A   F♯m   C♯m
It's not over, not over, not over, not over yet.

© Copyright 1993 Circa Music Limited.
Universal Music Publishing Limited (33.34%)/EMI Virgin Music Limited (66.66%).
All rights in Germany administered by Universal Music Publ. GmbH.
All Rights Reserved. International Copyright Secured.

Verse 2

        A   C♯m
Don't let me down, don't make a sound,

        A   C♯m
Don't throw it all a - way.

        A   F♯m   C♯m
Re - member me so tenderly,

        A   F♯m   C♯m
Don't let it slip a - way.

Link 2   ‖: A | F♯m | C♯m | C♯m :‖

Chorus 2   As Chorus 1

Link 3   ‖: A | F♯m | C♯m | C♯m :‖

              | A | A | A | A   ‖

Chorus 3   As Chorus 1

Outro   ‖: A | A* Amaj⁷ | A | A* Amaj⁷:‖ *Play 4 times*

              | A   ‖

Jessica

Words & Music by
Dan Hetherton, Ed Minton, Alex Davies, Paul Ali & Ed 'Teddy' Hetherton

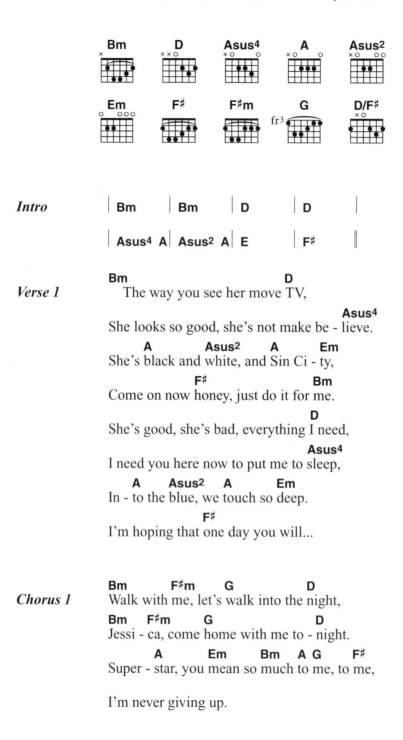

Intro

| Bm | Bm | D | D | |

| Asus4 A | Asus2 A E | F♯ | ‖

Verse 1

Bm   D
  The way you see her move TV,
                                              Asus4
She looks so good, she's not make be - lieve.
          A   Asus2   A   Em
She's black and white, and Sin Ci - ty,
                        F♯   Bm
Come on now honey, just do it for me.
                                        D
She's good, she's bad, everything I need,
                                            Asus4
I need you here now to put me to sleep,
          A   Asus2   A   Em
In - to the blue, we touch so deep.
                    F♯
I'm hoping that one day you will...

Chorus 1

Bm   F♯m   G   D
Walk with me, let's walk into the night,
Bm   F♯m   G   D
Jessi - ca, come home with me to - night.
            A   Em   Bm A G   F♯
Super - star, you mean so much to me, to me,

I'm never giving up.

© Copyright 2007 Copyright Control.
All Rights Reserved. International Copyright Secured.

Verse 2

<pre>
Bm   D
    Let's fight, tonight you're my dark angel,
                                      A
Let's go and run till we trip and we fall.
                                          Em
So take the sky, 'cause the world's too small,
                 F♯
And follow you with the Fantastic Four.
Bm   D   A   Em
(For) the first time I stood staring down across the floor.——
        F♯   Bm
Now walk with me to - night.
</pre>

Chorus 2   As Chorus 1

Interlude
<pre>
| Bm | Bm | D | D |

| A | A | F♯ | F♯   ‖
F♯
I'm never giving up.
</pre>

Chorus 3   As Chorus 1

Chorus 4
<pre>
Bm   F♯m   G   D
Walk with me, let's walk into the night,
Bm   F♯m   G   N.C.
Jessi - ca, come home with me tonight.
D   A   Em   Bm   A G F♯
Super - star, you mean so much, to me.——
</pre>

Solo
<pre>
| Bm | F♯m | G | D |

| Bm | F♯m | G | D   ‖
</pre>

Chorus 5
<pre>
D   A   Em   D/F♯   G   F♯
Super - star, you mean so much to me, to me,

I'm never giving up.
</pre>

Listen Up!

Words & Music by
Mary Beth Patterson, Nathan Howdeshell & Hannah Billie

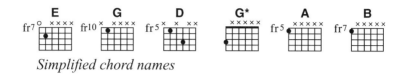

Simplified chord names

Intro |E |E G D|E |E G D|

|E |E G D|E |E   ‖

Link 1
E   G D E   G D
Ooh, ooh,   ooh.
E   G D E
Ooh, ooh,   ooh.

Verse 1
E   G D
I warned you, you didn't believe me.
E   G D
I warned you, you didn't believe me.
E   G D
I warned you, you didn't believe me.
E
I warned you, and now you're caught.

Bridge 1
E   G D
  There's some people that you just can't trust,
E   G D
  Some people talk way too much.
E   G D
  Take my advice and listen up,
E   N.C.
  Don't be a fool like the rest of us,

Now listen up.

© Copyright 2006 Chrysalis Music Limited.
All Rights Reserved. International Copyright Secured.

Pre-chorus 1

```
E G D    E            G D
```
Ooh, on the playground.
```
E G D    E
```
Ooh, on the playground.
```
                              N.C.           E  G
```
You learn so much, now listen up.
```
D          E      G
```
Now gather round,
```
D     E   G
```
Listen up,
```
D        E
```
Gather round now.

Chorus 1

```
E
```
One, two, three, take it from me,
```
                          G*   A  D   A B  E
```
Three, four, so much trou - ble in store.
```
                                      G* A
```
Four, five, get it right the first time, oh.
```
D        A    B  E
```
Count it with me now!

One, two, three, listen to me,
```
                          G*   A  D   A B  E
```
Three, four, so much trou - ble in store.
```
                                      G* A
```
Four, five, get it right the first time, oh.
```
D        A    B  E
```
Count it with me now.

Link 2

```
| E      | E  G  D | E      | E  G  D|

| E      | E  G  D | E      | E      ‖
```


Link 3

```
E  G  D E
```
Ooh,   ooh, ooh.
```
E  G  D E
```
Ooh,   ooh, ooh.

Verse 2

```
          E                                    G  D
            Everybody knows someone like that,
          E                                          G  D
            Who borrows money and won't pay you back.
          E                                    G  D
            They'll talk about you at the drop of a hat,
          E
            Lie about it to your face when they're caught.
```

Bridge 2

```
          E                                        G  D
            There's some people that you just can't trust,
          E                                  G  D
            Some people talk way too much.
          E                            G  D
            Take my advice and listen up,
          E                              N.C.
            Don't be a fool like the rest of us,

          Now listen up.
```

Pre-chorus 2

```
          E G  D     E           G  D
          Ooh,  on the playground.
          E  G  D     E
            Ooh,  on the playground.
                            N.C.              E  G
          You learn so much, now listen up.
          D         E         G
          Now gather round,
               D     E    G
          Now listen up,
          D      E
          Gather round now.
```

Chorus 2   As Chorus 1

Listening Man

Words & Music by
Paul Butler, Aaron Fletcher, Kristian Birkin, Michael Clevett, Warren Hampshire & Timothy Parkin

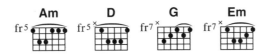

Intro

| Am | Am | Am | D | |
| G | Em | G | Em | |

Verse 1

G   Em
  Tell me something a - way from trouble
                   G   Em
And away from doubting.
G   Em   G   Em
  Tell me straight from the spirit, from the top of the mountain.
        G   Em
Let love be the reason between me and you,
        G   Em
As real as the morning, as fresh as the dew.
        G
If fear's got a hold then it's up to you,
        Em
It's a simple thing we've got to do.

Chorus 1

Am
  Just a listening man,
                D   Am
Try to under - stand.

Just a listening man,
               D
Doing the best I can.

© Copyright 2006 Beesource Products Limited.
Universal Music Publishing Limited. All rights in Germany administered by Universal Music Publ. GmbH.
All Rights Reserved. International Copyright Secured.

Verse 2

```
G                          Em
   Tell me something be - fore I stumble
              G          Em
And show my weakness.
G                    Em                    G          Em
   Tell me right on the line why I'm fighting for progress.
        G                      Em
I can hear there's a sound that's coming through,
        G                          Em
There's a pulse in the ground, so what we gonna do?
        G
You can have all your dreams
                 Em
If you really believe in something that's something true.
```

Chorus 2

```
Am
   Just a listening man,
            D     Am
Try to under - stand.

Just a listening man,
            D     Am
Doing the best I can.

Just a listening man,
            D     Am
Try to under - stand.

Just a listening man,
                     D
Getting carried through this land.
```

Interlude   ‖: G | Em | G | Em :‖

52

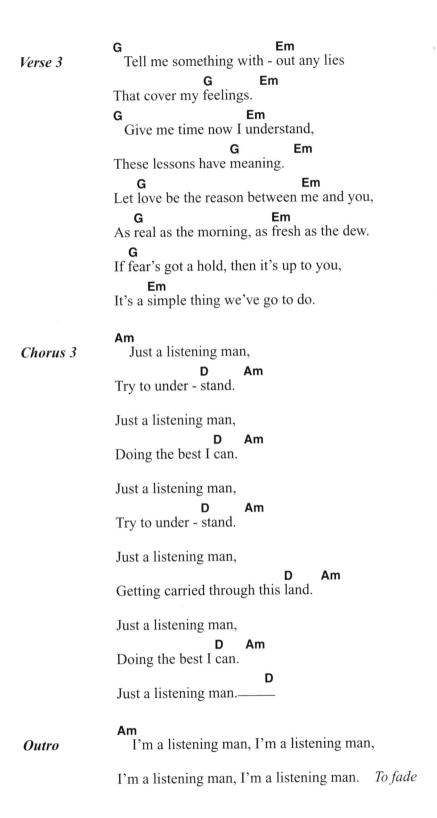

Verse 3

G   Em
Tell me something with - out any lies
           G   Em
That cover my feelings.
G   Em
Give me time now I understand,
               G   Em
These lessons have meaning.
   G   Em
Let love be the reason between me and you,
   G   Em
As real as the morning, as fresh as the dew.
   G
If fear's got a hold, then it's up to you,
       Em
It's a simple thing we've go to do.

Chorus 3

Am
Just a listening man,
             D   Am
Try to under - stand.

Just a listening man,
             D   Am
Doing the best I can.

Just a listening man,
             D   Am
Try to under - stand.

Just a listening man,
                   D   Am
Getting carried through this land.

Just a listening man,
             D   Am
Doing the best I can.
                   D
Just a listening man._____

Outro

Am
I'm a listening man, I'm a listening man,

I'm a listening man, I'm a listening man. *To fade*

53

Mammoth

Words & Music by
Paul Banks, Carlos Dengler, Daniel Kessler & Samuel Fogarino

Chord diagrams:
Doct (fr7), G5 (fr3), F5, A/E, B♭5 (fr6), A5 (fr5)
D (fr5), D6 (fr7), F#m/C# (fr4), A5* (fr7), D♭/F (fr8), G5* (fr10), A/C#
B♭ (fr6), Asus4 (fr5), Dm/C, Dm/A (fr6), Cadd9, Dm, G7

Intro ‖ Doct | Doct | Doct | Doct ‖

Verse 1

Doct
Spare me the suspense,

Spare me the suspense.

I got no currency, but I'm heaven sent.
G5   F5   A/E   Doct
So spare me __ the sus - pense,
G5   F5   A/E   Doct
Just spare me __ the sus - pense.
G5   B♭5   A5
Hey lady wraith, I so hope you try, you're late,
                              Doct
Baby you know it's your time.

Link 1 | Doct | Doct | Doct | Doct ‖
                                              (And I)

Chorus 1
G5   F5
And I won't let you sit by, so cold in the pitch night,
A/E   Doct
A - lone, you can't make a - mends.
G5   F5
And I won't let you sit by, so cold in the pitch night,
A/E   Doct
We should dance like two fucking twins.
G5   B♭5   A5   D
Just spare me __ the sus - pense.

© Copyright 2007 Kobalt Music Publishing Limited.
All Rights Reserved. International Copyright Secured.

| Link 2 | | D | | D | | D | | F#m/C# | ||
| | | | | | | | | | (There are) |

Bridge 1

               D   D6   F#m/C#

There are seven ancient pawn shops along the road, ——

                  B♭5   A5   F#m/C#

I know seven aching daddies you may want to know. ——

Interlude 1

Doct A5*   D♭/F G5*
Ooh, —— right on.

Doct A5*   D♭/F G5*   (Doct)
Ooh, —— ooh, ooh, —— ooh, ooh.

| Link 3 | | Doct | | Doct | | Doct | | Doct | ||
| | | | | | | | | | (Hey lady) |

Verse 2

               Doct

Hey lady wraith, oh baby, I can't deny,

I got a taste, a taste, a taste and it's time.

Chorus 2

              G5   F5

And I won't let you sit by, so cold in the pitch night,

               A/E   Doct

A - lone, you can't make a - mends.

              G5   F5

And I won't let you sit by, so cold in the pitch night,

               A/E   Doct

It's e - nough with this fucking in - cense.

              G5   B♭5   A5   D

Just spare me —— the sus - pense.

Bridge 2

               D   F#m/C#

There are seven ancient pawn shops along the road,

                          D   D6 F#m/C#

Oh, I know seven aching daddies you may want to know.

                  B♭5   A5   A/C#

When you've played your heart out, you made me turn —— around.

Interlude 2

Doct A5*   D♭/F G5*
Ooh, —— right on.

Doct A5*   D♭/F G5*
Ooh, —— ooh, ooh, —— ooh,

Doct A5*   D♭/F G5*
Ooh, —— ooh, ooh.

Bridge 3

B♭
Wait, oh you froze in the night,

    Asus4
You're late, there's a hole in the sky.

   Dm/C
No haste, no lesson, no lie,

  B♭
Got a taste, that I can't deny.

    Dm/A
And you wait 'til you know that it's time.

   Cadd9
You wait, 'til you know that it's time.

  B♭
You wait, 'til you know that it's time.

Dm/A
You wait, 'til you know that it's time.

Dm/C
You say to me, set black fires, do you know?

  G7
You say to me, set black fires.

Outro

| Dm | Dm | Dm | Dm | |

| Dm | Dm | Dm | Dm | |

| Dm | ‖

56

Misery Business

Words & Music by
Hayley Williams, Joshua Farro & Taylor York

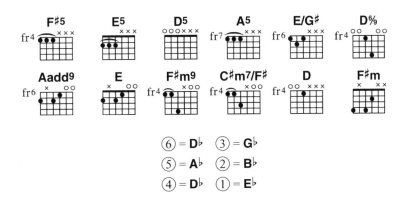

$6 = D\flat$ $3 = G\flat$
$5 = A\flat$ $2 = B\flat$
$4 = D\flat$ $1 = E\flat$

Intro

| F♯5 | E5 | F♯5 | D5 | |

| F♯5 | E5 | F♯5 | A5 E/G♯| F♯5 | ‖

| F♯5 | E5 | F♯5 | D5 | |

| F♯5 | E5 | F♯5 | A5 E/G♯‖

Verse 1

F♯5   E5   F♯5
  I'm in the business of misery, let's take it from the top,
             D5   F♯5
She's got a body like an hourglass that's ticking like a clock.
        E5   F♯5
It's a matter of time before we all run out,
         A5   E/G♯
When I thought he was mine, she caught him by the mouth.
F♯5   E5   F♯5
  I waited eight long months, she finally set him free,
        D5   F♯5
I told him I can't lie, he was the only one for me.
         E5
Two weeks and we had caught on fire,
      F♯5   A   E/G♯ F♯5 E5
She's got it out for me, but I wear the biggest smile.

© Copyright 2007 Copyright Control/W.B. Music Corporation/But Father I Just Want To Sing.
Copyright Control (50%)/Warner/Chappell Music Limited (50%).
All Rights Reserved. International Copyright Secured.

Chorus 1

D%   Aadd⁹   E
Whoa, I never meant to brag,

     F♯m⁹   C♯m7/F♯   D%
But I got him where I want him now.

         Aadd⁹   E
Whoa, it was never my intention to brag,

    F♯m⁹   C♯m7/F♯   D
To steal it all a - way from you now.

          F♯m   E
But God does it feel so good,

             F♯m   D
'Cause I got him where I want him now.

               F♯m   E
And if you could then you know you would,

      F♯m   E
'Cause God it just feels so....

Link 1

| F♯5 | E5 | F♯5 | D5   ‖
            It just feels so good.

Verse 2

F♯5   E5   F♯5
     Second chances they don't ever matter, people never change,

                       D5
Once a whore, you're nothing more,

               F♯5
I'm sorry that'll never change.

           E5
And about forgive - ness,

                   F♯5
We're both supposed to have ex - changed,

                A5   E/G♯   F♯5
I'm sorry honey, but I passed up, now look this way!

                   E5   F♯5
Well there's a million other girls who do it just like you,

               D5   F♯5
Looking as innocent as possible to get to who

                         E5   F♯5
They want and what they like, it's easy if you do it right.

                 A   E/G♯   F♯5   E5
Well I refuse, I re - fuse, I re - fuse!

Chorus 2   As Chorus 1

Bridge | D% | Aadd⁹ | E | |

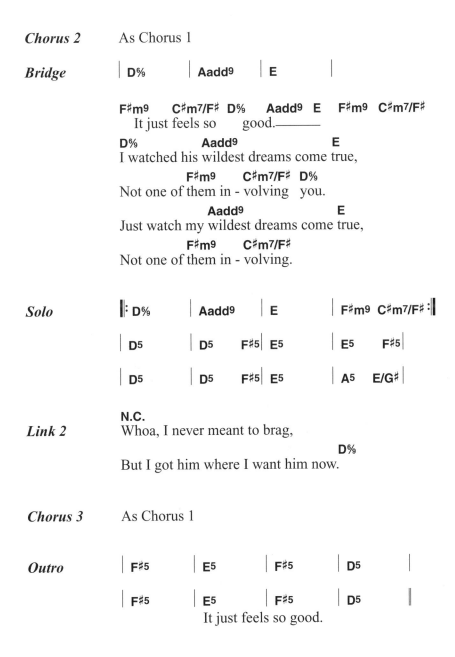

F♯m⁹   C♯m7/F♯ D%   Aadd⁹ E   F♯m⁹ C♯m7/F♯
  It just feels so   good.————
D%   Aadd⁹   E
I watched his wildest dreams come true,
        F♯m⁹   C♯m7/F♯ D%
Not one of them in - volving you.
        Aadd⁹   E
Just watch my wildest dreams come true,
        F♯m⁹   C♯m7/F♯
Not one of them in - volving.

Solo   ‖: D% | Aadd⁹ | E | F♯m⁹ C♯m7/F♯ :‖

| D5 | D5   F♯5| E5 | E5   F♯5|

| D5 | D5   F♯5| E5 | A5   E/G♯|

Link 2
N.C.
Whoa, I never meant to brag,
                                 D%
But I got him where I want him now.

Chorus 3   As Chorus 1

Outro | F♯5 | E5 | F♯5 | D5 |

| F♯5 | E5 | F♯5 | D5 ‖
             It just feels so good.

Men's Needs

Words & Music by
Gary Jarman, Ross Jarman & Ryan Jarman

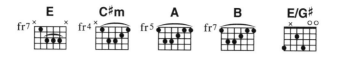

Intro   ‖: E | E | C♯m | C♯m   :‖

Verse 1

E
Have you noticed I've never been im - pressed
                                                          C♯m

                                                        E
By your friends from New York and London.
                                    C♯m
I'll level accusations like the press,

Till you realise that you've dressed yourself in tatters.

Chorus 1

(C♯m)   A   E
Because the man's needs, man's needs are full of greed,

Are full of greed.
        A   E
A man's needs, man's needs are lost on me.
        A   E
A man's needs, man's needs are full of greed, full of greed.
        A   B
A man's needs.——

Verse 2

E   C♯m
I'm not bothered what you say or how you dress,
                                                        E
I'm a mess so you've always seemed inviting.
                                    C♯m
But really this all seems quite meaning - less,

And I remember that you never seem to see...

© Copyright 2007 Chrysalis Music Limited.
All Rights Reserved. International Copyright Secured.

Chorus 2

   (C♯m)   A   E
The fact that man's needs, man's needs are full of greed,

Are full of greed.
  A   E
A man's needs, man's needs are lost on me.
  A   E
A girl's needs, girl's needs, just don't agree, just don't agree,
      A   B
With a man's needs.——

Solo

| E | E | C♯m | C♯m | |

| E/G♯ | E/G♯ | A | B | |

| E | E | C♯m | C♯m | |

| E/G♯ | A | B | B | ‖

Verse 3

E   C♯m
   Have you noticed I've never been im - pressed
                                        E
By your friends from New York and London?
                              C♯m
But really this all seems quite meaning - less,

When I remember that you never seem to see.

Chorus 3

   (C♯m)   A   E
   The excuse that man's needs, man's needs are full of greed,

Are full of greed.
  A   E
A man's needs, man's needs are lost on me.
      A   E
You say a man's needs, man's needs ap - ply to me,
  C♯m   A   B
I don't agree, a man's needs,——
        (E)
Oh, oh.——

Outro

‖: E | E | E | E :‖

1234

Words & Music by
Sally Seltmann & Feist

D5   D5/C♯   Bm   G   D   Em   A

⑥ = D   ③ = G
⑤ = A   ② = B
④ = D   ① = E

Intro

| D5 D5/C♯ | Bm G | D5 D5/C♯ | Bm G ‖

Verse 1

D5   D5/C♯   Bm   G
One, two, three, four, tell me that you love me more.

D5   D5/C♯   Bm   G
Sleepless long nights, that is what my youth was for.

D   Em   Bm   G
Old teen - age hopes are a - live at your door,

D   Em   Bm   G
Left you with nothing but they want some more.

Chorus 1

A   G
Oh, oh, oh, you're changing your heart.

A   G
Oh, oh, oh, you know who you are.

Verse 2

D5   D5/C♯   Bm   G
Sweetheart, bitter heart, now I can tell you apart.

D5   D5/C♯   Bm   G
Cosy and cold, put the horse be - fore the cart.

D   Em   Bm   G
Those teen - age hopes who have tears in their eyes,

D   Em   Bm   G
Too scared to own up to one lit - tle lie.

Chorus 2   As Chorus 1

© Copyright 2007 Candid Music Publishing Limited (75%)/
BMG Music Publishing Limited (25%).
All Rights Reserved. International Copyright Secured.

Bridge 1

D5   D5/C♯   Bm   G
One, two, three, four, five, six, nine or ten,

D5   D5/C♯   Bm   G   D5
Money can't buy you back the love that you had then.

| D5 D5/C♯ | Bm G | D5 D5/C♯ | Bm G |
(then.)

D5   D5/C♯   Bm   G
One, two, three, four, five, six, nine or ten,

D5   D5/C♯   Bm   G   (D5)
Money can't buy you back the love that you had then.

| D5 D5/C♯ | Bm G | D5 D5/C♯ | Bm G   ‖
(then.)

Chorus 3

A   G
Oh, oh, oh, you're changing your heart.

A   G
Oh, oh, oh, you know who you are.

A   G
Oh, oh, oh, you're changing your heart.

A   G   D Em Bm G
Oh, oh, oh, you know who you are.————

          D Em Bm G
Who you are.————

Interlude

‖: D5 Em | Bm G | D5 Em | Bm G :‖ *Play 3 times*

Outro

D   Em Bm
For,

G   D   Em Bm G
For the teen - age boys,

                 D   Em Bm
They're breaking your heart.

G   D   Em Bm G
For the teen - age boys,

                 D   D5/C♯ Bm G
They're breaking your heart.

| D5 D5/C♯ | Bm G | D   ‖

The Pretender

Words & Music by
Dave Grohl, Taylor Hawkins, Nate Mendel & Chris Shiflett

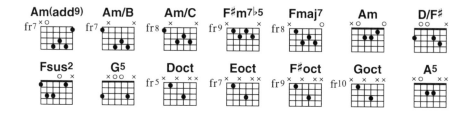

Intro | Am(add9) | Am/B Am/C| F#m7♭5 | Fmaj7 ‖

Am(add9)   Am/B Am/C   F#m7♭5 Fmaj7
Keep you in the dark, you   know they all pre - tend,

Am(add9)   Am/B Am/C F#m7♭5 Fmaj7
Keep you in the dark and   so it   all be - gan.

Verse 1

Am
Send in your skeletons,

                                    D/F# Fsus2
Sing as their bones go marching in a - gain.

Am
   They need you buried deep,

                                    D/F#
The secrets that you keep are ever ready.

Fsus2   G5 Am
Are you ready?

I'm finished making sense,

                                D/F#   Fsus2 G5
Done pleading ignorance, that whole de - fence.

Am
   It's been an infinity but, the wheel is spinning me,

      D/F#   Fsus2
It's never ending, never ending,

Doct Eoct F#oct Goct
Same old   sto - ry.

© Copyright 2007 Universal Music Publishing Limited (87.5%)/Copyright Control (12.5%).
All rights in Germany administered by Universal Music Publ. GmbH.
All Rights Reserved. International Copyright Secured.

Chorus 1

Am
What if I say I'm not like the others?
                                         D/F♯
What if I say I'm not just another one in your place?

You're the pretender.
Fsus2
What if I say I will never surrender?
Am
What if I say I'm not like the others?
                                         D/F♯
What if I say I'm not just another one in your place?

You're the pretender.
Fsus2
What if I say that I'll never surrender?

Link 1 | **A5** | **A5**   ‖

Verse 2

Am   **D/F♯**   **Fsus2** **G5**
  In time or so I'm told, I'm just another soul for sale, oh well.
Am
  The page is out of print, we are not permanent,
       D/F♯   **Fsus2**
We're temporary temporary,
Doct Eoct F♯oct Goct
Same old sto - ry.

Chorus 2

Am
What if I say you're not like the others?
                                           D/F♯
What if I say you're not just another one in your place?

You're the pretender.
Fsus2
What if I say that I'll never surrender?
Am
What if I say you're not like the others?
                                           D/F♯
What if I say you're not just another one in your place?

You're the pretender.
Fsus2   **Doct Eoct F♯oct Goct**
What if I say I will never surren - der?

Link 2 | **A⁵** | **A⁵** | **A⁵** | **A⁵**   ‖

Bridge
Am
I'm the voice inside your head you refuse to hear,

I'm the face that you have to face, mirroring your stare.

I'm what's left, I'm what's right, I'm the enemy,

I'm the hand that'll take you down, bring you to your knees.

So who are you?

Yeah, who are you?

Yeah, who are you?

Yeah, who are you?

Interlude
Am(add⁹)   **Am/B Am/C**   **F♯m⁷♭5 Fmaj⁷**
Keep you in the dark, you   know they all pre - tend.

Chorus 3
Am
What if I say I'm not like the others?
                                      D/F♯
What if I say I'm not just another one in your place?

You're the pretender.
Fsus²
What if I say I will never surrender?
Am
What if I say you're not like the others?
                                      D/F♯
What if I say you're not just another one in your place?

You're the pretender.
Fsus²
What if I say that I'll never surrender?

Chorus 4

Am
What if I say I'm not like the others?
　　　　　　　　　　　　　　　　D/F♯
What if I say I'm not just another one in your place?

You're the pretender.

Fsus²
What if I say I will never surren - der?

Am
What if I say you're not like the others?
　　　　　　　　　　　　　　　　D/F♯
What if I say you're not just another one in your place?

You're the pretender.

Fsus²　　　　　　　　　　**Doct Eoct F♯oct Goct**
What if I say that I'll never surren - der?

Outro

　　　　A⁵
So who are you?

Yeah, who are you?

Yeah, who are you?

Saturday Superhouse

Words & Music by
Simon Neil

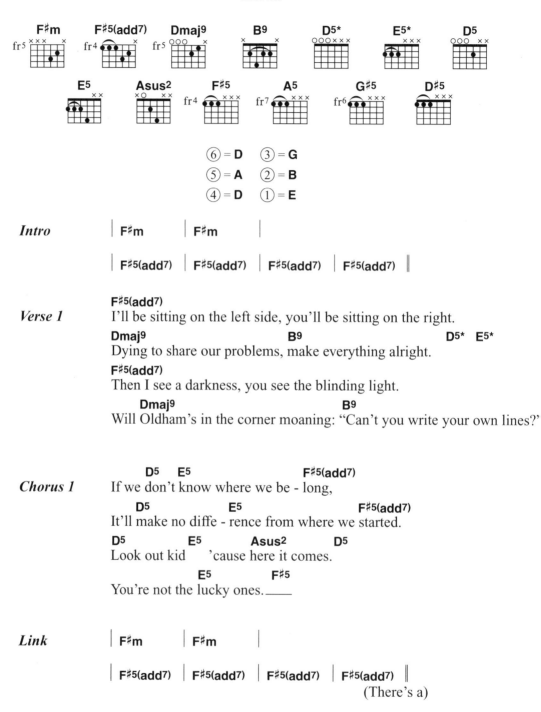

Intro | F#m | F#m |

| F#5(add7) | F#5(add7) | F#5(add7) | F#5(add7) ‖

Verse 1

F#5(add7)
I'll be sitting on the left side, you'll be sitting on the right.
Dmaj9   B9   D5* E5*
Dying to share our problems, make everything alright.
F#5(add7)
Then I see a darkness, you see the blinding light.
    Dmaj9   B9
Will Oldham's in the corner moaning: "Can't you write your own lines?'

Chorus 1

     D5 E5   F#5(add7)
If we don't know where we be - long,
    D5   E5   F#5(add7)
It'll make no diffe - rence from where we started.
D5   E5   Asus2   D5
Look out kid   'cause here it comes.
          E5   F#5
You're not the lucky ones._____

Link | F#m | F#m |

| F#5(add7) | F#5(add7) | F#5(add7) | F#5(add7) ‖
                       (There's a)

© Copyright 2006 Good Soldier Songs Limited.
Universal Music Publishing Limited. All rights in Germany administered by Universal Music Publ. GmbH.
All Rights Reserved. International Copyright Secured.

Verse 2
F♯5(add7)
There's a dozen corpses on the left side, I swear one's smiling at me.

Dmaj9   B9   D5*   E5*
Compliments on your confession baby, wow you really showed me.

F♯5(add7)
You think that you're full of conviction, really you're just trying to survive.

Dmaj9   B9
Tie them up then spit them out, it's good to help the boy shine.

Chorus 2   As Chorus 1

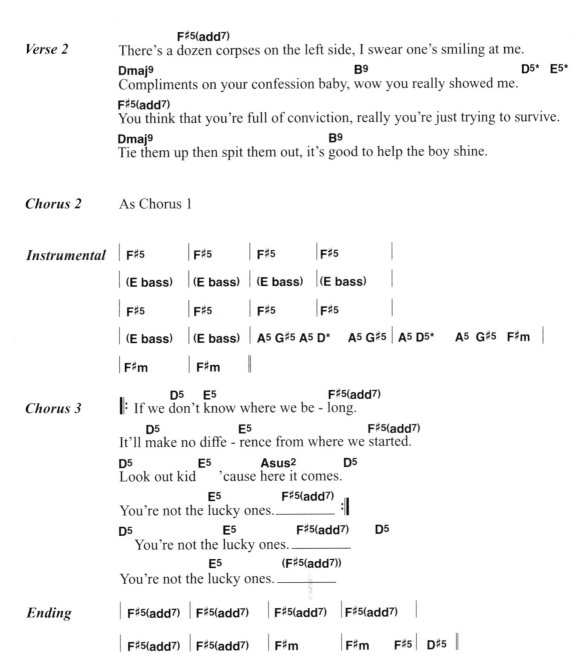

Instrumental | F♯5 | F♯5 | F♯5 | F♯5 |

| (E bass) | (E bass) | (E bass) | (E bass) |

| F♯5 | F♯5 | F♯5 | F♯5 |

| (E bass) | (E bass) | A5 G♯5 A5 D*   A5 G♯5 | A5 D5*   A5 G♯5 F♯m |

| F♯m | F♯m   ‖

Chorus 3
                       D5   E5   F♯5(add7)
‖: If we don't know where we be - long.

              D5   E5   F♯5(add7)
It'll make no diffe - rence from where we started.

D5   E5   Asus2   D5
Look out kid   'cause here it comes.

                    E5   F♯5(add7)
You're not the lucky ones._____ :‖

D5   E5   F♯5(add7)   D5
   You're not the lucky ones. _____

                    E5   (F♯5(add7))
You're not the lucky ones. _____

Ending | F♯5(add7) | F♯5(add7) | F♯5(add7) | F♯5(add7) |

| F♯5(add7) | F♯5(add7) | F♯m | F♯m   F♯5 | D♯5 ‖

She Builds Quick Machines

Words & Music by
Matt Sorum, Duff 'Rose' McKagan, Scott Weiland & David Kushner

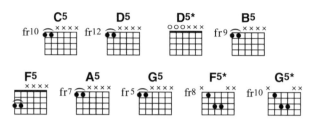

⑥ = D   ③ = G
⑤ = A   ② = B
④ = D   ① = E

riff 1 _____

Intro   ‖: C5 D5 D5* C5 D5 D5* C5 D5 | B5 D5 D5* B5 F5 D5* F5 D5* :‖

Play 8 times

riff 1   **riff 1**
Verse 1   Hold fast little love,

                                    riff 1
Burn strong, let it roam.

                              riff 1
Ice cold desert snow,

                                    riff 1
She build a quick dream.

                                    riff 1
Sister keep her motor clean,

                                       riff 1
Sunday visits and a wet machine.

                                 riff 1
She's always quick to fight,

We'll break her through tonight.

A5 G5 C5 F5 G5 F5   G5 A5 D5*   A5 G5   C5
Pre-chorus 1   I   could feel it   when you pull straight down,
F5 G5 F5 G5 A5 D5*
A5 G5 C5 F G5 F5 G5 A5 D5*   A5   G5   F5   G5
I   can feel it   when they stood their ground.——

© Copyright 2007 Chrysalis Music Limited/Ready Set Go Publishing/
Pimp Music/Dracsorum Music/Slash And Cash Publishing/DTK Music.
Chrysalis Music Limited.
All Rights Reserved. International Copyright Secured.

riff 1

Chorus 1   Roll over, right,

           riff 1

Keep it through the night, right, right,

           riff 1

Keep it through the night.

                 riff 1

Right in my sight, keep it through the night,

I'll smash right through your spotlight.

riff 1   **riff 1**

Verse 2   She ran away to Texas,

          riff 1

To keep away the excess,

       riff 1   **riff 1**

Old ex in Vegas, dope, back taxes.

             riff 1

She burned through inheritance,

          riff 1

Danced across America,

          riff 1

At the all-night sex show so far from home.

A^5 G^5 C^5 F^5 G^5 F^5 G^5 A^5 D^{5*} A^5 G^5 C^5

Pre-chorus 2 I   could feel it when you pull straight down,

F^5 G^5 F^5 G^5 A^5 D^{5*}

A^5 G^5 C^5 F G^5 F^5 G^5 A^5 D^{5*} A^5 G^5 F^5 G^5

    I   can feel it when they stood their ground.——

riff 1

Chorus 2   Roll over, right,

          riff 1

Keep it through the night, right, right,

          riff 1

Keep it through the night.

                riff 1

Right in my sight, keep it through the night,

I'll smash right through your spotlight.

Link | **D5*** | **D5*** | **D5*** | **D5***   ‖

D5*

Bridge   What you give is what you take,

What you bleed is what you break.

I bleed for you,
             F5*   **G5***
I'd steal for you,
    D5*   **F5***   **G5***
I'd take, I'd take,
    D5*   **F5***
I'd take, I'd take,
   G5*   **F5***
I'd take, I'd take,
   G5*   **(riff 1)**
I'd take, I'd take.

Solo   ‖: **riff 1** | **(riff 1)** | **riff 1** | **(riff 1)** |

            | **F5** | **F5** | **G5** | **G5**   :‖

Pre-chorus 3   As Pre-Chorus 1

Chorus 3   As Chorus 1

Sheila

Words by Jim Parker, Jamie Treays & John Betjeman
Music by Jim Parker & Jamie Treays

G   Em   D   C   Am

Chorus 1

      G   Em
Sheila goes out with her mate Stella,

                          D
It gets poured all over her fella,

                                        C
'Cause she says, "Man he ain't no better

                               G
Than the next man kicking up fuss."

                                 Em
Drunk, she stumbles down by a river,

                    D
Screams calling "London."

                             C   G
None of us heard her coming; I guess the carpet weren't rolled out.

Interlude

      G
Oh when my love, my darling,

            Em
You've left me here alone,

      D
I'll walk the streets of London,

            C
Which once seemed all our own.

      G
The vast suburban churches,

            Em
To - gether we have found:

                D
The ones which smelt of gaslight,

            C
The ones in incense drowned.

© Copyright 2006 Zomba Music Publishers Limited(87.5%)/Copyright Control (12.5%).
All Rights Reserved. International Copyright Secured.

Verse 1

       G
Her lingo went from the Cockney to the Gringo,

Em
Anytime she sing a song the other girls sing along.

     D
And tell all the fellas that the lady is single,

      C
A fickle way ta tickle on my young man's ting.

     G
She's up for doing what she like, any day, more like the night!

       Em
She drowned drunk the sorrows, that she stole, bought, borrowed.

     D
She didn't like fights but at the same time understood that,

C
Fellas will be fellas till the end of time.

Link 1

     G
   Good heavens you boys,

Em
 Blue-blooded murder of the English tongue!

     D   **C**
Blup!

Verse 2
(chords as
Verse 1)

Jack had a gang that he called the Many Grams,
He was known as Smack Jack the Cracker man.
In life he was dealt some shit hands,
But the boys got the back now.
And Jay went the same way as Micky and Dan,
Dependent man's upon the he - roin.
And man, Lisa had a baby with Sam,
And now Jack's on his own man.
Well done, Jack! Glug down that cider
You're right – she's a slut and you never fucking liked her.
Not like, what, he stopped so shocked,
'Cause it turns out the last dance killed the pied piper.
Tough little big man, friends with your daughters,
Only 'cause they drive him to pick up all his quarters.
Crawler, lager lout brawlers, fall to the floor think they're free,
But they ain't near da border.
Too young gunned down are by your hell fire corner,
Always did a favour but never took a order.
Be - have young scallywag! A fine young Galahad,
Glad-ragged up, but only ever getting fag hags.
Hung on his shoulder, cheap price shop tag,
Slag better understand he came for the glamour.
But this town's original, superficial the issue,
For one dear Jack had thirty-five doppelgangers.

Chorus 2   As Chorus 1

Link 2   **(Am)**   **(Em)**
                    It's over man, it's over! LONDON!

Verse 3   So this a short story about the girl Georgina,
(chords as   Never seen her worse, clean young mess,
Verse 1)   Under stress at best, but she's pleased to see you.
                    With love, God Bless, we lay her body to rest.
                    Now it all dear started with Daddy's alcoholic,
                    Lightweights, chinking down, numbing his brain.
                    And the doctor said he couldn't get the heart dear started,
                    Now beat up, drugged up, she feeling the strain.
                    She says, "In a rut, what the fuck I supposed to do?"
                    Suck it up, start, stop, keep running through.
                    "True, but you try, it ain't easy to do."
                    She been buckle-belt, beaten from the back like a brat,
                    Dunno where she going, but she know where she at.
                    So Georgie, it's time to chain react,
                    But the truth is, you know, she probably fought back.
                    Tears stream down her face, she screamed away:
                    "When I fall, no one catch me,
                    Alone, lonely, I'll overdose slowly, get scared, I'll scream and shout."
                    But you know it won't matter she'll be passing out.
                    I said giggidibidup, just another day,
                    An - other sad story that's tragedy.
                    Para - medic announced death at ten thirty,
                    Rip it up, kick it, to spit up the views.

Chorus 3   As Chorus 1

Chorus 4   As Chorus 1

She's Got You High

Words & Music by
James New, James Arguile, Niall Buckler, Oliver Frost & Gareth Jennings

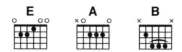

Intro

| E | E | E | E |
| A | A | E | E ‖

Verse 1

E
She's got you high and you don't even know yet,

She's got you high and you don't even know yet.
      A
The sun's in the sky, it's warming up your bare legs,
E
You can't deny you're looking for the sunset.

Verse 2

E
She's got you high and you don't even know yet,

She's got you high and you don't even know yet.
      A
It's the search for the time before it leaves without you,
     E
Have you lost your mind or has she taken all of yours too?

Chorus 1

   E
‖: What's this about? I figured love would shine through,

We've lost romance, this world, it's turned so see-through.
A
Open your mind, believe it's gonna come true,
     E   B E
Keep romance alive and hope she's gonna tell you. :‖

© Copyright 2006 Universal Music Publishing Limited.
All rights in Germany administered by Universal Music Publ. GmbH.
All Rights Reserved. International Copyright Secured.

Verse 3

E
She's got you high and you don't even know yet,

She's got you high and you don't even know yet.

A
The sun's in the sky, it makes for happy endings,

E
You can't deny you want the happy ending.

Chorus 2

E
What's this about? I figured love would shine through,

We've lost romance this world, it's turned so see through.

A
Open your mind, believe it's gonna come true,

E   B   E
Keep romance alive and hope she's gonna tell you.

Bridge

(E)
She's got you high.

A   E
She's got you high.

B   E
She's got you high.

Chorus 3

E
‖: What's this about? I figured love would shine through,

We've lost romance this world, it's turned so see through.

A
Open your mind, believe it's gonna come true,

E
Keep romance alive and hope she's gonna tell you. :‖

Link

B   E
She's got you high.

Chorus 4

E
What's this about? I figured love would shine through,

We've lost romance this world has turned so see through.

A
Open your mind, believe it's gonna come true,

E
Keep romance alive and hope she's gonna tell you.

Outro

B   E
She's got you high.

Smokers Outside The Hospital Doors

Words & Music by
Tom Smith, Russell Leetch, Chris Urbanowicz & Ed Lay

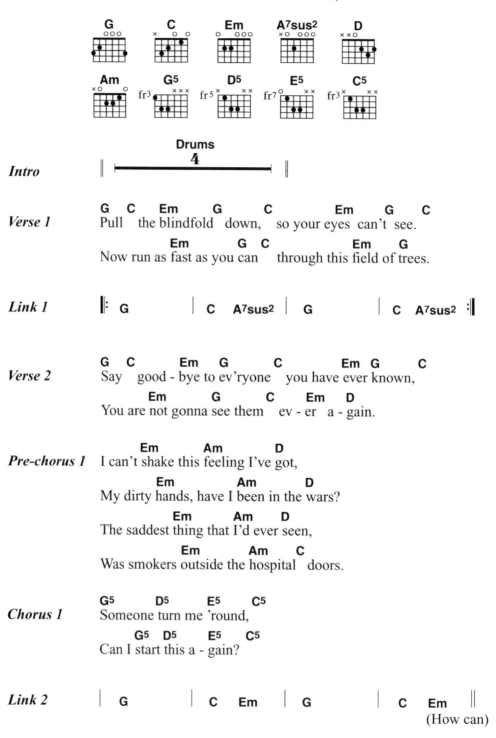

Intro

Verse 1
```
G   C   Em    G         C            Em    G   C
Pull the blindfold down,  so your eyes can't see.
              Em        G  C              Em    G
Now run as fast as you can    through this field of trees.
```

Link 1
‖: G | C A7sus2 | G | C A7sus2 :‖

Verse 2
```
G   C      Em   G        C           Em  G      C
Say  good - bye to ev'ryone    you have ever known,
            Em        G      C    Em    D
You are not gonna see them    ev - er  a - gain.
```

Pre-chorus 1
```
           Em        Am       D
I can't shake this feeling I've got,
           Em        Am       D
My dirty hands, have I been in the wars?
             Em        Am      D
The saddest thing that I'd ever seen,
               Em          Am     C
Was smokers outside the hospital   doors.
```

Chorus 1
```
G5        D5       E5      C5
Someone turn me 'round,
       G5 D5     E5      C5
Can I start this a - gain?
```

Link 2
| G | C Em | G | C Em ‖
                                (How can)

© Copyright 2007 Soul Kitchen Music Limited.
Kobalt Music Publishing Limited.
All Rights Reserved. International Copyright Secured.

78

Verse 3

   (Em)   G   C Em   G   C   Em   G   C
How can we   wear our smiles   with our mouths wired shut?

              Em   G   C   Em   D
'Cause you stopped us from singing.

Pre-chorus 2   As Pre-chorus 1

Chorus 2

G⁵   D⁵   E⁵   C⁵
Someone turn me 'round,

        G⁵ D⁵   E⁵   C⁵
Can I start this a - gain?

        G⁵   D⁵   E⁵   C⁵
Now, someone turn us a - round,

        G⁵ D⁵   E⁵   C⁵   G
Can we start this a - gain?

Bridge

            (G)   Am   Em   C
We've all been changed from what we were,

        G   Am   Em   C
Our broken hearts left smashed on the floor.

           G   Am   Em   C
I can't be - lieve you   if I can't hear you,

           G   Am   Em C
I can't be - lieve you   if I can't hear you.

Instrumental

Bass & drums

‖ |—— 4 ——| ‖

‖: G | C A⁷sus² | G | C A⁷sus² :‖

Interlude

          G⁵   D⁵   E⁵   C⁵
‖: We've all been changed from what we were,

        G⁵   D⁵   E⁵   C⁵
Our broken hearts smashed on the floor. :‖

Chorus 3
*(with backing
vocals from
interlude)*

G⁵   D⁵   E⁵   C⁵
Someone turn me 'round,

        G⁵ D⁵   E⁵   C⁵
Can I start this a - gain?

        G⁵   D⁵   E⁵   C⁵
Now, someone turn us around,

        G⁵ D⁵   E⁵   C⁵
Can we start this a - gain?

Suburban Knights

Words & Music by
Richard Archer

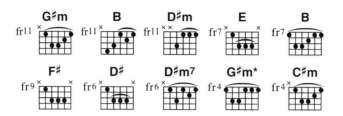

Intro

    G♯m   B   D♯m G♯m
Hey.———————

    B   D♯m G♯m
Oh.———————

    B   D♯m G♯m
Ah.———————

    B   D♯m
Hey.———————

Verse 1

G♯m
  Suburban days, they last so long,

In shop and office, we sing our song. We all sing:
E   B   E   B   E
  "We ain't got nothing,   nothing to do."
       B   E   F♯   G♯m
A big fat nothing,   nothing for me nothing for you.
     E   G♯m   E
Ah, oh.

Verse 2

G♯m
  Suburban dreams, just out of reach,

Work till you die, that's what they teach you at school.
E   B   E   B
  With that in mind,   what's there to lose?
E   B E   F♯   G♯m
  My friends and I   doped up on T.V., fags and booze.
     E
Ah, oh.

© Copyright 2007 BMG Music Publishing Limited.
All Rights Reserved. International Copyright Secured.

Chorus 1

D♯
Hear them all singing:

G♯m B/D♯   D♯m   G♯m
Hey,—— we're the ones that you've for - gotten,

        B/D♯   D♯m   G♯m
Oh,—— but we will not be de - nied.

        B/D♯   D♯m   G♯m
Ah,—— coming out of the shadows,

        B/D♯   D♯m   G♯m
Hey,—— yeah, yeah, we rock the satellite.

Guitar solo | G♯m | G♯m | G♯m | G♯m   ‖

Verse 3

G♯m
    Suburban nights, they get so hot,

People get angry, we sing our song, we all sing.

E   B   E   B   E
    But global terror they say,   we are at war,

                  B   E
But ain't got time for that 'cause

                      F♯   G♯m
Those bills keep dropping through my door.

        E
Ah, oh.

Chorus 2

D♯
Hear them all singing:

G♯m B/D♯   D♯m   G♯m
Hey,—— we're the ones that you've for - gotten,

        B/D♯   D♯m   G♯m
Oh,—— out of mind and out of sight.

        B/D♯   D♯m   G♯m
Ah,—— coming out of the shadows,

        B/D♯   D♯m   G♯m
Hey,—— yeah, yeah, we rock the satellite.

Link 2 | G♯m | G♯m   ‖

Bridge

D#m7   G#m*   D#m7
And all these people who   criticize us, well,

                                          G#m*
We're only saying what we're seeing with our own eyes.

E   B   E   B   E
  This one way system it ain't,   it ain't para - dise,

               B   E   F#   G#m
Not every - body   wants to race, wants to fight.

      E
Ah, oh.

      C#m   D#
Ah, oh, ah, oh.

Chorus 3

(D#)
Hear them all singing:

G#m   B/D#   D#m   G#m
  Hey,—— we're the ones that you've for - gotten,

      B/D#   D#m   G#m
Oh,—— but we will not be de - nied.

      B/D#   D#m   G#m
Ah,—— coming out of the shadows,

      B/D#   D#m   G#m
Hey,—— yeah, yeah, we rock the satellite.

      B/D#   D#m   G#m
Hey,—— we're the ones that you've for - gotten,

      B/D#   D#m   G#m
Oh,—— out of mind and out of sight.

      B/D#   D#m   G#m
Ah,—— coming out of the shadows,

      B/D#   D#m
Hey,—— coming live via satellite.

Interlude

‖: G#m | G#m | G#m | G#m   :‖

‖: G#m B/D#| D#m G#m | G#m B/D# | D#m G#m:‖

Outro

G#m   B/D# D#m G#m
  Hey.————

      B/D# D#m G#m
Oh.————

      B/D# D#m G#m
Ah.————

      B/D# D#m
Hey.————

‖: G#m | G#m | G#m | G#m   :‖

Tarantula

Words & Music by
Billy Corgan

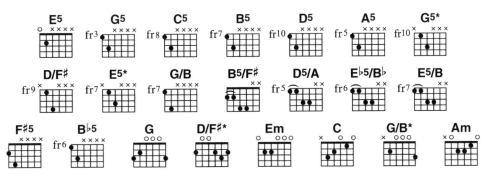

Tune guitar down a semitone

Intro
| E5 | | E5 | E5 | E5 | E5 | |

Verse 1

E5   G5   C5
I don't want to fight,

E5   G5   C5
Every single night,

E5   G5   C5   E5   G5 C5
Everything I want is in your eyes.

E5   G5   C5
You and me go back,

   E5   G5   C5
To places I don't know to care,

   E5   G5   C5   E5
The spoils of all I got were left for scraps.

Pre-chorus 1

B5   D5
 Don't let me say this,

  C5   A5
But you're no worse than me,

  B5 D5
It's cra - zy.

Chorus 1

   G5*   D/F#   E5*
We are the real, if real ever was, and just because,

   C5   G/B   A5
We are the real, they feel we have e - nough.

   G5*   D/F#   A5
We are the real, 'cause someone gave us up.

© Copyright 2007 Universal Music Publishing Limited.
All rights in Germany administered by Universal Music Publ. GmbH.
All Rights Reserved. International Copyright Secured.

Verse 2

E5   G5   C5   E5   G5 C5
I want to be there when you're happy.

E5   G5   C5   E5
I want to love you when you're sad.

G5   C5   E5
Can't stand the morning rain?

   G5   C5   E5
Get out I'll take your place then.

G5   C5   B5/F♯ D5/A E♭5/B♭ E5/B
Can't stand the blazing sun?

     G5   F♯5 A5 B♭5
Then close your eyes you'll see

   B5   E5
The angel dust.

Solo

| E5 | G5 C5 | E5 | G5 C5 |

| E5 | G5 C5 | E5 | E5   ‖

Verse 3

E5   G5   C5
I don't want to be,

E5   G5   C5
Anything be - lieved,

   E5   G5   C5   E5   G5 C5
A million watts of sound can't com - pare.

E5   G5   C5
Come along you'll see the world,

     E5   G5   C5
The pulse ripples, the crowd un - furls.

     E5   G5   C5   B5 D5
The current starts to flow and then you're on.

Pre-chorus 2

              C5   A5   B5 D5
Oh it's the white hot soul they want to sing for.

Chorus 2

G5*   D/F♯   E5*
We are the real, if real ever was, and just because,

    C5   G/B   A5
We are the ruin of every living soul.

      G5*   D/F♯   A5
We are surreal, 'cause someone gave us up.

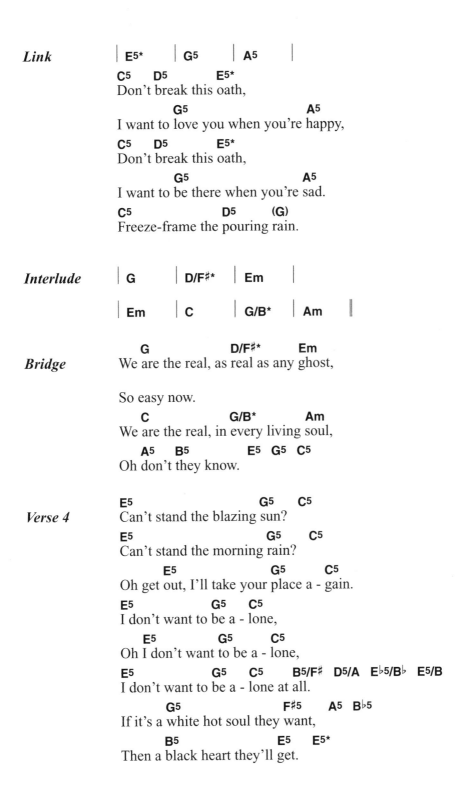

Link | E5* | G5 | A5 |

C5   D5   E5*
Don't break this oath,

        G5   A5
I want to love you when you're happy,

C5   D5   E5*
Don't break this oath,

        G5   A5
I want to be there when you're sad.

C5   D5   (G)
Freeze-frame the pouring rain.

Interlude | G | D/F♯* | Em |

| Em | C | G/B* | Am ‖

        G   D/F♯*   Em
Bridge   We are the real, as real as any ghost,

So easy now.

        C   G/B*   Am
We are the real, in every living soul,

    A5   B5   E5 G5 C5
Oh don't they know.

E5   G5   C5
Verse 4   Can't stand the blazing sun?

E5   G5   C5
Can't stand the morning rain?

        E5   G5   C5
Oh get out, I'll take your place a - gain.

E5   G5   C5
I don't want to be a - lone,

    E5   G5   C5
Oh I don't want to be a - lone,

E5   G5   C5   B5/F♯ D5/A E♭5/B♭ E5/B
I don't want to be a - lone at all.

        G5   F♯5   A5 B♭5
If it's a white hot soul they want,

    B5   E5   E5*
Then a black heart they'll get.

85

Thnks Fr Th Mmrs

Words & Music by
Peter Wentz, Andrew Hurley, Joseph Trohman & Patrick Stumph

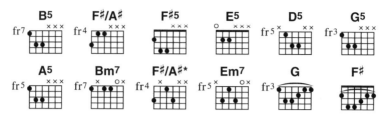

Tune guitar down a semitone

Intro | B5 | B5 | B5 | B5 |‖

Verse 1
B5   F#/A#
I'm gonna make you bend and break, (it sent you to me without wings).
              F#5   E5
Say a prayer, but let the good times roll.
   D5   F#/A#
In case God doesn't show. (Let the good times roll, let the good times roll)
      B5
And I want these words to make things right,
   F#/A#   F#5   E5
But it's the wrongs that make the words come to life.
        D5
Who does he think he is?
       F#/A#
If that's the worst you've got, better put your fingers back to the keys.

Chorus 1
B5   G5
One night and one more time,
E5   G5   F#/A#   B5
Thanks for the memories, even though they weren't so great.
   G5   A5
He tastes like you only sweet - er.
    B5   G5
One night, yeah and one more time,
E5   G5   F#/A#
Thanks for the memories, thanks for the memories.
B5   G5   A5
See he, tastes like you only sweet - er, oh.

Link 1 | B5 | B5 | B5 | B5 |‖

© Copyright 2007 Sony/ATV Songs LLC/Chicago X Softcore Songs, USA.
Sony/ATV Music Publishing (UK) Limited.
All Rights Reserved. International Copyright Secured.

Verse 2

B5   F♯/A♯

Been looking forward to the future,

                F♯5   E5

But my eyesight is going bad.

   D5   F♯/A♯

In this crystal ball,

    B5

It's always cloudy except for, (except for),

          F♯/A♯   F♯5   E5

When you look into the past. (Look into the past).

      D5   F♯/A♯

One night stand. (One night stand).

Chorus 2   As Chorus 1

Bridge

      Bm7   F♯/A♯   Em7   G   F♯

They say I only think in the form of crunching num - bers

Bm7   F♯/A♯   Em7   G   F♯

  In hotel rooms, col - lecting page-six lov - ers.

Bm7   F♯/A♯*

Get me out of my mind,

Em7   G   F♯

Get you out of those clothes.

Bm7   F♯/A♯*   Em7   F♯5

  I'm a line a - way from getting you into the mood.

Chorus 3

B5 N.C.

One night and one more time,

Thanks for the memories, even though they weren't so great.

He tastes like you only sweeter.

    B5   N.C.

One night,   yeah and one more time,

Thanks for the memories, thanks for the memories.

                          A5

See he, tastes like you only sweet - er, oh.

Chorus 4   As Chorus 1

Ending | B5   ‖

3's & 7's

Words & Music by
Josh Homme, Joey Castillo & Troy Van Leeuwen

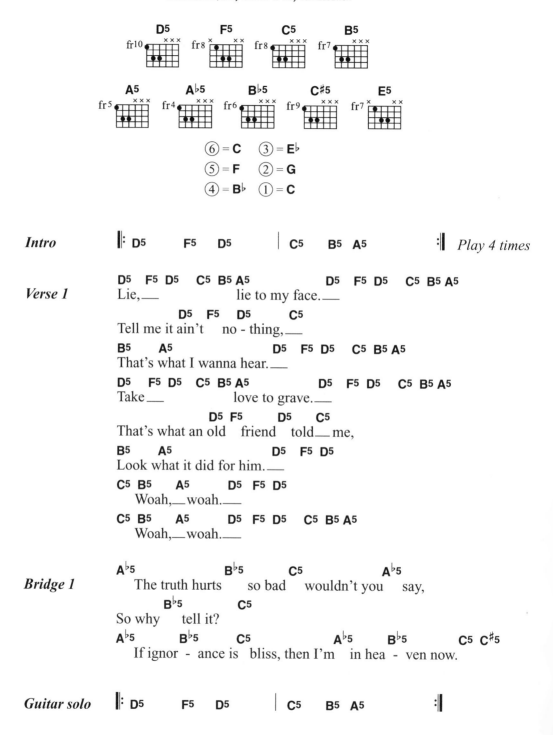

Intro ‖: D5   F5   D5 | C5   B5   A5 :‖ *Play 4 times*

Verse 1
D5 F5 D5   C5 B5 A5   D5   F5 D5   C5 B5 A5
Lie,—   lie to my face.—
                    D5 F5 D5   C5
Tell me it ain't   no - thing,—
B5   A5   D5   F5 D5   C5 B5 A5
That's what I wanna hear.—
D5 F5 D5   C5 B5 A5   D5   F5 D5   C5 B5 A5
Take—   love to grave.—
                    D5 F5   D5   C5
That's what an old   friend   told—me,
B5   A5   D5   F5 D5
Look what it did for him.—
C5 B5   A5   D5 F5 D5
     Woah,—woah.—
C5 B5   A5   D5 F5 D5   C5 B5 A5
     Woah,—woah.—

Bridge 1
Ab5   Bb5   C5   Ab5
     The truth hurts   so bad   wouldn't you   say,
         Bb5   C5
So why   tell it?
Ab5   Bb5   C5   Ab5   Bb5   C5 C#5
     If ignor - ance is   bliss, then I'm   in hea - ven now.

Guitar solo ‖: D5   F5   D5 | C5   B5   A5 :‖

© Copyright 2007 Board Stiff Music/Magic Bullet Music/More Kick And Snare Music, USA.
Universal Music Publishing Limited. All rights in Germany administered by Universal Music Publ. GmbH.
All Rights Reserved. International Copyright Secured.

Verse 2

D5 F5 D5   C5 B5 A5   D5 F5 D5   C5 B5 A5
Run,—   you'll never escape.—

              D5 F5   D5   C5
You see you'll go   no - where,

B5 A5   D5 F5 D5   C5 B5 A5
So new you appear.—

D5   F5 D5   C5 B5 A5   D5 F5 D5   C5 B5 A5
Broke,—   laid to waste.—

            D5   F5 D5   C5
Turn into sweet   no - things,—

B5 A5   D5 F5 D5
  Kiss you goodbye. —

‖: C5 B5   A5   D5 F5 D5 :‖ *Play 3 times*
    Woah,—woah.—

C5 B5   A5   D5 F5 D5   C5 B5 A5
  Woah,—woah.—

Bridge 2   As Bridge 1

Middle

A5   C5   B5   D5   C♯5
   Keep go - ing o - ver and o - ver again,—

              E5   F5   D5   A5
The never ending pla - ces I've never been.—

          C5   B5   D5   C♯5
No - one's— catching on— call - ing my bluff.—

              E5   F5   D5   A5
The Devil made me ho - lier than I've ev - er been.—

              C5   B5   D5   A5
What'd you do?— Say— it with— a smile,—boy,

      F5   D5   A5
Mak - ing us all forget.

              C5   B5   D5   A5
What'd you do?— Say— it with— a smile,—boy,

      F5   D5   A5
Mak - ing us all forget.—

F5   D5   A5
Making us all forget.—

F5   D5   A5   F5 D5
Making us all forget.—

Bass solo
                  4
Interlude   ‖———————————‖

Outro   ‖: D5   F5   D5 | C5   B5 A5   :‖ *Play 8 times*

What I've Done

Words & Music by
Chester Bennington, Mike Shinoda, Rob Bourdon, Joseph Hahn, Brad Delson & Dave Farrell

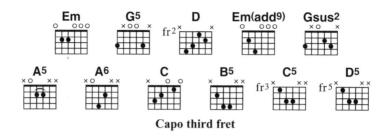

Capo third fret

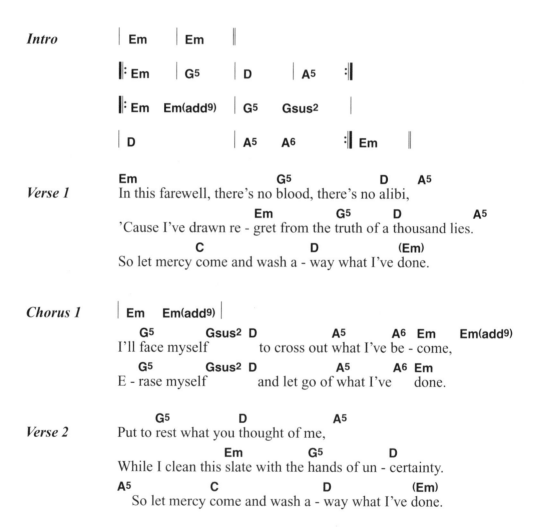

Intro | Em | Em ‖

‖: Em | G5 | D | A5 :‖

‖: Em Em(add9) | G5 Gsus2 |

| D | A5 A6 :‖ Em ‖

Verse 1
Em   G5   D   A5
In this farewell, there's no blood, there's no alibi,
                              Em   G5   D   A5
'Cause I've drawn re - gret from the truth of a thousand lies.
                        C   D   (Em)
So let mercy come and wash a - way what I've done.

Chorus 1 | Em Em(add9) |

      G5   Gsus2 D   A5   A6 Em   Em(add9)
I'll face myself   to cross out what I've be - come,
      G5   Gsus2 D   A5   A6 Em
E - rase myself   and let go of what I've   done.

Verse 2
            G5   D   A5
Put to rest what you thought of me,
                       Em   G5   D
While I clean this slate with the hands of un - certainty.
A5   C   D   (Em)
So let mercy come and wash a - way what I've done.

© Copyright 2007 Zomba Songs Incorporated/Big Bad Mr. Hahn Music/Rob Bourdon Music/
Kenji Kobayashi Music/Chesterchaz Publishing/Nondisclosure Agreement Music/
Pancakey Cakes Music, USA. Zomba Music Publishers Limited.
All Rights Reserved. International Copyright Secured.

Chorus 2

| Em   Em(add9) |

    G5   Gsus2 D   A5 A6 Em   Em(add9)
I'll face myself   to cross out what I've be - come,

    G5   Gsus2 D   A5   B5   C5   D5 (Em)
E - rase myself   and let go of what   I've   done.

Solo

| Em   Em(add9) | G5   Gsus2 | D | A5   A6 |

| Em   Em(add9) | G5   Gsus2 | D | A5   B5   ‖

Bridge

    C5   D5   Em   Em(add9)
For what I've done

    G5   Gsus2 D   A5   A6   Em   Em(add9)
I start again   and whatever pain may come,

    G5   Gsus2 D   A5   A6   (Em)
To - day this ends,   I'm forgiving what I've done.

Chorus 3

| Em   Em(add9) |

    G5   Gsus2 D   A5 A6 Em   Em(add9)
I'll face myself   to cross out what I've be - come,

    G5   Gsus2 D
E - rase myself

                    A5   A6   Em   Em(add9) G5 Gsus2 D
And let go of what I've done.

Outro

    A5   A6   Em   Em(add9) G5 Gsus2 D
What I've done,

              A5   Em
Forgiving what I've done.

91

The World Is Outside

Words & Music by
Robert Smith, Simon Pettigrew, Edward Harris & Mark Treasure

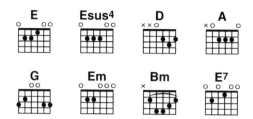

Capo first fret

Intro   ‖: E | Esus⁴ | E | Esus⁴ :‖

Verse 1
```
       E                          D
    Where'd your sense of ad - venture go?
     A                          E
  You sit at home with dinner on a tray,
                      D     A
  The world is out - side.
     E                        D
    Do you remember how it used to be?
       A                              E
  At seventeen, we've never been the same,
                      D     A
  Forgotten our lines.
```

Chorus 1
```
            G                            A          Em
  She said, we could do anything, we can do   anything.
        Bm          D          A                Em
  Oh,— open your eyes; the world is outside your door.
        Bm              D       A
  Oh,— don't tell me your   story if you don't have one.
```

Link 1 | E | Esus⁴ | A | A   ‖

© Copyright 2006 Perfect Songs Limited.
All Rights Reserved. International Copyright Secured.

Verse 2

    E   **D**
The last Monday in January is

    A   **E**
Ap - parently the worst day of the year,

           D   **A** **E**
Maybe they're right.

                   D
I don't even know what day it is,

    A   **E**
I'm tired of this, wish we were kids a - gain,

           D   **A**
With time on our side.

Chorus 2

       G   **A**   **Em**
She said, we could do anything, we can do anything,

   Bm   **D**   **A**   **Em**
Oh,— open your eyes; the world is outside your door.

   Bm   **D**   **A**   **Em**
Oh,— you're kidding your - self 'cause every - thing else is old.

   Bm   **D**   **A**   **Em**
Oh,— open your eyes; the world is outside your door.

   Bm   **D**   **A**
Oh,— don't tell me your story if you don't have one.

Bridge

G   **Bm** **G**
  Oh.———

    Bm **G** **Bm**
Oh.—

    Em
Oh.—

Link 2

‖: **Em** | **Bm** | **D** | **A**   :‖

Chorus 3

Em **Bm**   **D**   **A**   **Em**
  Oh,— open your eyes; the world is outside your door.

   Bm   **D**   **A**   **Em**
Oh,— you're kidding your - self 'cause every - thing else is old.

   Bm   **D**   **A**   **Em**
Oh,— you're taking your time; the world is outside your door.

   Bm   **D**   **A**
Oh,— don't tell me your story if you don't have one.

Outro

‖: **E7** | **E7** | **E7** | **E7** :‖ **Em**   ‖

Torn On The Platform

Words & Music by
Jack Peñate

Intro

A   C#m7   D   E
Once more just be - fore I'm leaving, torn on the platform.

A   C#m7   D   E
Once more just be - fore I'm leaving, torn on the platform.

               D   C#m7
'Cause I'll miss you and I love you,

    Bm7   Amaj7
I know this is over for now.

               D   C#m7
'Cause I'll miss you, oh, how I'll miss you,

    Bm7   Amaj7
You're not my girl, you're my town.

Link 1
Double time

‖: A | C#m7 | D | E   :‖

| Esus4 | Esus4 | Esus4 ‖

Verse 1
Half time

  A   C#m7   D
  A weekend away, leave the city today,

           E   A
Don't want the big smoke to leave me behind.

               C#m7   D
The train leaves at two, platform three Waterloo,

E   A
50p to the tramp makes me feel kind.

© Copyright 2007 Universal Music Publishing Limited.
All Rights Reserved. International Copyright Secured.